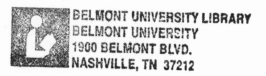

Strategies for
Recruitment,
Retention and
Graduation of
Minority Nurses
in Colleges
of Nursing

Hattie Bessent,
EdD, RN, FAAN
Editor

Published by
American Nurses Publishing
600 Maryland Ave., SW
Suite 100 West
Washington, DC 20024

D-100 1M 11/97

Contents

Foreword

Dr. Hattie Bessent, an American Nurses Foundation Distinguished Scholar, has assembled the most current information on the successful recruitment, retention, and graduation of minority nurses in colleges of nursing. The investigation was stimulated by the Institute of Medicine study, *Balancing the Scales in Opportunity: Ensuring Racial and Ethnic Diversity in the Health Professions*, that presented means to ensure racial and ethnic diversity in the health professions, but focused primarily on medicine. This report provides a framework for meeting the challenge of creating a more diverse, humane and caring health care system. Dr. Bessent and a select group of scholars collaborated to address one of the most compelling issues facing health care—the rapidly expanding demographics of those requiring care versus the static demographics of those providing care. Despite nursing's legacy of advocacy and partnership, the growth of baccalaureate and higher degree prepared minorities in nursing has been minimal.

Historically, nurses have had a unique and strong relationship with the consumer. Consequently, nursing is well positioned to provide care for the increasing number of minorities who are emerging in communities throughout the country. With the recent demise of affirmative action in some states, the likelihood of closing the gap between the color of health care consumers and health care providers has become more elusive.

The report extends the work of the Institute of Medicine study in that more definitive information is provided about how racial and ethnic diversity can be achieved in the profession. It is presented in three parts. In Part One, the problem and related issues are presented with a historical overview and a general perspective of the need to ensure more ethnic diversity in nursing. Part Two describes the barriers that exist to increasing the number of minority nurses. Cultural dimensions of several minority groups—African, Asian, Hispanic, and Native Americans—are highlighted. In Part Three, the ethical, philosophical, psychological, and economic issues affecting the ability to increase the number of minority nurses are addressed. Exemplary strategies for moving minority nurses from recruitment to graduation are presented. The issues, suggestions, strategies, and ideas of Dr. Bessent, which are reflected throughout the report, provide a dynamic framework and a guide to a problem that has not been resolved in nursing. The report offers another opportunity for nursing to create an action agenda to increase the number of minority nurses participating in the health care delivery system.

Beverly Malone, PhD, RN, FAAN
President, American Nurses Association

Fran Hicks, PhD, RN, FAAN
Past President, American Nurses Foundation

Acknowledgments

Strategies for Recruitment, Retention and Graduation of Minority Nurses in Colleges of Nursing began when two colleagues had a conversation about minority nurses. This discussion led to the recent report of the Institute of Medicine and ended by saying a project should be done to include nurses.

Special thanks should be given to the American Nurses Foundation for providing financial support. I am grateful for their generosity, and recognition that in order to build an effective health care system, minority nurses must be accessible. I am also thankful to the American Nurses Association (ANA) and the National League for Nurses (NLN) for their support.

This monograph benefitted greatly from collaborations with colleagues across the country. I thank them for their time and expertise. All their commitment, knowledge, articles and books, and teaching skills caused this monograph to become a reality. Physicians, nurses, psychologists, sociologists and social workers across the country—thank you for your consistent support throughout this project. Your discussions, debates and convincing criticism led to the clarity of my ideas.

Faculties, deans and students from schools of nursing across the country—I thank all of you for your insights and suggestions that led me to see things from a variety of viewpoints.

Dr. Juanita Fleming was a consultant, critic and editor throughout this project and I am extremely grateful to her for her patience, suggestions and editorial support. She was with me during each phase of the development of this monograph. She worked closely with Dr. Richard Kriyscio in the analysis and interpretation of all data.

I wish to thank the ANA Minority Fellows who sent me periodicals, reviewed background material, and wrote thoughtful summaries.

My secretarial staff and the secretarial staff across the country—I am grateful for their wonderful help in transcribing tapes, collecting documents, and typing and retyping the manuscript.

Thanks to the people of the Low Country of South Carolina. This environment clarified views after numerous debates and conversations with experts from many areas. The plan for this project, including the issues that confront the

viii	
Acknowledgments	

profession and how the plight of the minority nurse, which is a great resource for the profession, should be presented was born in the Low Country.

I thank those who offered their homes to me for meetings with professional colleagues from many areas—to have a chance to debate, listen, and come away with books, periodicals, and tapes that caused me to think and read.

Finally, I must thank one who is closest to me, my sister, Marion, who has given me full support during this project. She has given me her time, thoughts, and judgment from the beginning to the end. Thanks also to my loving, deceased Grandmother whose presence kept me on the course.

Hattie Bessent

Hattie Bessent, EdD, RN, FAAN
Editor

Contributors

Myrtle K. Aydelotte, PhD, FAAN
   Professor and Dean Emeritus, University of Iowa College of Nursing, Iowa City, IA 52242, 21 Menlo Place, Rochester, NY 14620

Gordon L. Berry, EdD
   Professor, Graduate School of Education and Information Studies, University of California, Los Angeles (UCLA), 405 Hilgard Avenue, Los Angeles, CA 90024

Hattie Bessent, EdD, RN, FAAN
   Deputy Executive Director Emerita, Director of Minority Fellowship Program, 5622 Sophist Circle South, Jacksonville, FL 32219

Peter I. Buerhaus, PhD, RN, FAAN
   Director, Harvard Nursing Research Institute, Assistant Professor of Health Policy and Management, Harvard School of Public Health, Cambridge, MA 02115

Lisa Cruz-Avalos, MSN, RN, CS
   Nursing Consultant, Department of Health and Rehabilitative Services, 5600 Fisher Lane, Parklawn Building 9-36, Rockville, MD 20857

Juanita W. Fleming, PhD, RN, FAAN
   Professor of Nursing and Special Assistant, Academic Affairs, Office of the President, University of Kentucky 40506-0032

Faye Gary, EdD, RN, FAAN
   Distinguished Professor, College of Nursing, University of Florida, Gainesville, FL 32610

Fran Hicks, PhD, RN, FAAN
   Professor, Portland State University, Past President, American Nurses Foundation, 600 Maryland Avenue, SW, Suite 100 West, Washington, DC 20024-2571

James Jones, PhD
   Professor, Research, University of Delaware, Newark, DE 19716-2577

Audrey Koertvelyessy, MSN, RN, PNP
   Captain, Nursing Consultant, Health Resources and Services Administration, Department of Health and Professions, Division of Nursing, Department of Health and Rehabilitative Services, 5600 Fisher Lane, Parklawn Building 9-36, Rockville, MD 20857

Phyllis B. Kritek, PhD, RN, FAAN
   Chair, Mental Health/Management, Doctoral Program Director, School of Nursing, Florida Thelma Hall Distinguished Professor of Nursing, Professor, Mental Health/Management, The University of Texas

x

Contributors

School of Nursing at Galveston, The University of Texas School of Nursing, Room 3.211, 1100 Mechanic Street, Galveston, TX 77555-1029

Beverly Malone, PhD, RN, FAAN
President, American Nurses Association, 600 Maryland Avenue, SW, Suite 100 West, Washington, DC 20024-2571

Freida Outlaw, DNSc, RN, CS
Associate Professor, College of Nursing, University of Pennsylvania, 458 Duck Pond Lane, Haverford, PA 19041

Lucius Outlaw, PhD
Professor of Philosophy, Haverford College, 458 Duck Pond Lane, Haverford, PA 19041

Michael Pallak, PhD
Executive Director Emeritus, American Psychological Association, San Francisco, CA, 705 Winchester Dr., Burlingame, CA 94010

Bobbie Perdue, PhD, RN
Associate Professor, College of Nursing, Syracuse University, Syracuse, NY 13244-3240

Timothy Ready, PhD
Assistant Vice President for Community and Minority Programs, Association of American Medical Colleges, 2450 N Street, NW, Washington, DC 20037

Romeria Tidwell, PhD
Professor, Graduate School of Education and Information Studies, University of California, Los Angeles (UCLA), 405 Hilgard Avenue, Los Angeles, CA 90024

Workshop Participants

Myrtle K. Aydelotte, PhD, FAAN
  Professor and Dean Emeritus, University of Iowa College of Nursing,
    Iowa City, IA 52242, 21 Menlo Place, Rochester, NY 14620

Gordon L. Berry, EdD
  Professor, Graduate School of Education and Information Studies,
    University of California, Los Angeles (UCLA), 405 Hilgard Avenue,
    Los Angeles, CA 90024

Hattie Bessent, EdD, RN, FAAN
  Deputy Executive Director Emerita, Director of Minority Fellowship
    Program, 5622 Sophist Circle South, Jacksonville, FL 32219

Peter I. Buerhaus, PhD, RN, FAAN
  Director, Harvard Nursing Research Institute, Assistant Professor of Health
    Policy and Management, Harvard School of Public Health, Cambridge,
    MA 02115

Doris Campbell, PhD, RN, FAAN
  Professor and Director of Diversity Initiates,University of South
    Florida,College of Medicine,12901 Bruce B. Downs Boulevard,
    Tampa, FL 33612

M. Elizabeth Carnegie, DPA, RN, FAAN
  Editor Emerita, Journal of Nursing Research

Lisa Cruz-Avalos, MSN, RN, CS
  Nursing Consultant, Department of Health and Rehabilitative Services,
    5600 Fisher Lane, Parklawn Building 9-36, Rockville, MD 20857

Vernice Fergerson, MS, FAAN
  Senior Fellow, Fagin Family Chair in Cultural Diversity, University of
    Pennsylvania, College of Nursing, 132 Quincy Place NE,
    Washington, DC 20002

Juanita W. Fleming, PhD, RN, FAAN
  Special Assistant to the President for Academic Affairs, University of
    Kentucky, Room 7, Administration Building, Lexington, KY
    40506-0032

Faye Gary, EdD, RN, FAAN
  Distinguished Professor, College of Nursing, University of Florida,
    Gainesville, FL 32610

Sylvia Hart, PhD, RN
  Professor and Dean Emeritus, University of Tennessee, Knoxville
    College of Nursing, Knoxville, TN 37909

Fran Hicks, PhD, RN, FAAN
  Professor, Portland State University, Past President, American Nurses
    Foundation, 600 Maryland Avenue, SW, Suite 100 West,
    Washington, DC 20024-2571

James Jones, PhD
  Professor, Research, University of Delaware, Newark, DE 19716-2577

Audrey Koertvelyessy, MSN, RN, PNP
  Nursing Consultant, Department of Health and Rehabilitative Services,
    5600 Fisher Lane, Parklawn Building 9-36, Rockville, MD 20857

Phyllis B. Kritek, PhD, RN, FAAN
  Chair, Mental Health/Management, Doctoral Program Director, School of
    Nursing, Florence Thelma Hall Distinguished Professor of Nursing,
    Professor, Mental Health/Management, The University of Texas
    School of Nursing at Galveston, Room 3.211, 1100 Mechanic Street,
    Galveston, TX 77555-1029

Elaine Larson, PhD
  Dean, School of Nursing, Georgetown University, 3700 Reservoir Road,
    NW, St. Mary's Hall, Washington, DC 20007

Kem B. Louie, PhD, RN, CS, FAAN
  Professor and Chairperson, Graduate Nursing Program, College of Mount
    Saint Vincent, 6301 Riverdale Avenue, Bronx, NY 10471

Beverly Malone, PhD, RN, FAAN
  President, American Nurses Association, 600 Maryland Avenue, SW,
    Suite 100 West, Washington, DC 20024-2571

Doris Mosley, PhD, RN
  Dean, School of Nursing, University of District of Columbia,
    4201 Massachusetts Avenue, NW, Washington, DC 20016

Freida Outlaw, DNSc, RN, CS
  Associate Professor, College of Nursing, University of Pennsylvania,
    458 Duck Pond Lane, Haverford, PA 19041

Lucius Outlaw, PhD
  Professor of Philosophy, Haverford College, 458 Duck Pond Lane,
    Haverford, PA 19041

Michael Pallak, PhD
  Executive Director Emeritus, American Psychological Association,
    San Francisco, CA, 705 Winchester Dr., Burlingame, CA 94010

Bobbie Perdue, PhD, RN
  Associate Professor, College of Nursing, Syracuse University, Syracuse, NY
    13244

Robert V. Piemonte, EdD, RN, CAE, FAAN
  Consultant, 76 West 86th Street, New York, NY 10034

Dorothy L. Powell, EdD, RN, FAAN
  Dean, College of Nursing, Howard University, 501 Bryant Street, NW,
    Washington, DC 20059

Jeanne Spurlock, MD
  Psychiatrist—Retired, 1628-B Beekman Place, Washington, DC 20009

Dalmas A. Taylor, PhD
  Vice President for Academic Affairs, Lincoln University, Lincoln University,
    PA 19352

Romeria Tidwell, PhD
  Professor, Graduate School of Education and Information Studies,
    University of California, Los Angeles (UCLA), 405 Hilgard Avenue,
    Los Angeles, CA 90024
Irene Trowell-Harris, EdD, RN
  Director of Patient Care Inspections & Evaluation Division, Office of
    Healthcare Inspections (54C), Department of Veterans Affairs, 810
    Vermont Avenue, NW, Washington, DC 20420

Preface

Dr. Hattie Bessent has spent her entire professional life working on behalf of the training and inclusion of ethnic minority nurses in the delivery of health care to citizens of this country. This monograph is a comprehensive testament to her work for many years. Through her dedication, tireless energy and determination, Dr. Bessent has brought quality care, training opportunities, professional development and leadership training to hundreds of young men and women of color in the nursing profession. In spite of her long, tireless and effective work, she still understands that the job is not done. This monograph tells us some of the problems we still face, why we have to look at our public policy approaches differently, and how differences across cultural backgrounds present challenges as well as opportunities for our health care professions.

Dr. Bessent obtained her bachelor of science degree in nursing from Florida A&M University in 1959, and has worked as a nurse, or on behalf of nurses, ever since. Beginning as a psychiatric nurse in Jacksonville, Florida, after she earned her bachelor's degree, she served in a variety of academic settings, including assistant and associate professor of nursing at Florida A&M University and graduate dean of nursing at Vanderbilt University. Dr. Bessent has been active in research, most notably at the Institute of Human Resources project on Intellectual Stimulation and Families from 1962 to 1971 in Gainesville, Florida, as well as in a number of administrative positions and fellowships with the American Council on Education and at Harvard University. She has administered over $8 million in grants from the federal government and the Kellogg Foundation. All of these projects were designed to support the training of nurses of color in research and leadership, as well as clinical fields. Moreover, with support from the Kellogg Foundation, she focused on the development of leadership skills for women of color, and was impressed by the rapid development of those participants in their leadership skills and ambitions.

This outstanding record of service and professional contributions summarize Dr. Bessent's focused efforts on building the capacity of people of color to provide the services, research and leadership in our health care industry that raise the standard of health and well being of citizens of color in America. Given this long service and commitment, one could understand how she might be very excited to read the Institute of Medicine's Report, *Balancing the Scales of Opportunity in Health Care: Ensuring Racial and Ethnic Diversity in the Health Professions* (Lewin and Rice 1994). But it turned out that while the report could document large-scale efforts to balance those skills, opportunities in nursing education were not equally available. The report claimed the laudable efforts to increase minority participation in health care over the last 20 years.

Although we use the term minority to be inclusive of all ethnic non-White groups, the Institute of Medicine report limited it to African American, Hispanic, and American Indians (Fleming 1995). Members of these groups were most seriously underrepresented in health care. The need for better health care to these underserved communities of color led the committee to recommend a variety of interventions beginning as early as elementary school, partnerships between local, state, and federal agencies, joined by private foundations to provide the massive multilevel approach to this continuing problem. Although Dr. Bessent was pleased to see such prestigious bodies make such a cogent argument for the needs to which she had devoted her professional life, it was also clear that health care seemed in this report to refer primarily to the medical and dental professions (Fleming 1995).

It is to this gap of knowledge and opportunity for nurses of color that organized the writing of this monograph. Whatever under-representation of ethnic/racial minorities exists in the medical profession, the same problem exists in nursing as much, or more so. The Division of Nursing in the Health Resources and Services Administration reported that there were 2,115,815 registered nurses employed in nursing in 1966 (Division of Nursing 1996). Among these practicing nurses, 107,527 (4.2 percent) are African American, 40,559 (1.6 percent) are Hispanic, and 11,843 (.5 percent) are American Indian/Alaskan Native. The total number of practicing nurses then was less than 160,000 or less than 6 percent of all nurses. Since these three racial/ethnic groups make up nearly 30 percent of the U.S. population, and a much higher percentage of those in need of health care, the under-representation of nurses of color is very large.

By addressing the critical issues that restrict opportunities for people of color in nursing, as well as strategies to increase those opportunities, we will be better informed of the kind of interventions proposed by the Institute of Medicine report. Moreover, by examining those issues that affect the success of various programs directed at nurses of color in their education and employment in health care, we will aid in developing more sensitive and effective programs to meet the goals of a better health care industry. Finally, there can be no opportunity for persons who are unprepared. It is vital that the recruitment, retention, and graduation of minority nurses from colleges of nursing be invigorated with resources, dedication and commitment.

Dr. Bessent has worked with health care professionals across many disciplines in her many professional activities. Her colleagues in psychology, social work, sociology, philosophy, and medicine have all contributed to and been a part of her many efforts to improve the representation and leadership roles of nurses of color in health care. Dr. Bessent has called upon many of these friends and colleagues to contribute their expertise to this monograph through debates, workshops, and visits to schools around the country. The author provides an overview of problems, issues and prospects for addressing the needs of nurses of color.

Part One is a historical review and explains the impetus for this study. I don't believe one can understand fully attitudes, beliefs and opinions of the present unless they understand the past. That is one of the reasons the Institute of Medicine has initiated a call for a more systematic and sustained effort to ensure the continuous flow of ethnic minority nurses to choose careers in the health professions.

Part Two summarizes the general barriers minorities face in higher education. There is discussion of the philosophical issues also. This summary also includes a detail discussion from four minority nurse perspectives (Asian, African American, Hispanic, and Native American).

Part Three explores the broader context of the problems facing minority nurses. Really this is a problem confronting the entire nursing profession. Economics, ethics and psychosocial issues are just the beginning. Then developed strategies are presented. When strategies are presented, the discussion continues to the ingredients for success. Should we continue to stand still and pretend there is no problem or should we make at least one step in the direction of quality care for everyone? The implications and recommendations for nursing education are spelled out.

I am delighted to be part of this very important project and I am sure that when you have finished reading this book, the problems and approaches to their solutions will be clearer and the sense of progress palpable.

James M. Jones
American Psychological Association
University of Delaware

References

Division of Nursing. 1996. *Advance notes from the national sample survey of registered nurses*. Rockville, MD: Health Resources and Services Administration.

Fleming, J. W. 1955. *Balancing the scales of opportunity in healthcare: Ensuring racial and ethnic diversity in the health professions: A report from the Institute of Medicine, Healthcare Trends & Transition* 6: 24-32.

Lewin, M., & B. Rice., eds. 1994. *Balancing the scales of opportunity in healthcare: Ensuring racial and ethnic diversity in the health professions*. Washington, DC: National Academy Press.

The Gift Outright

Robert Frost

The land was ours before we were the land's.
She was our land more than a hundred years
Before we were her people. She was ours
In Massachusetts, in Virginia,
But we were England's, still colonials,
Possessing what we still were unpossessed by,
Possessed by what we now no more possessed.
Something we were withholding made us weak
Until we found out that it was ourselves
We were withholding from our land of living,
And forthwith found salvation in surrender.
Such as we were we gave ourselves outright
(The deed of gift was many deeds of war)
To the land vaguely realizing westward,
But still unstoried, artless, unenhanced,
Such as she was, such as she would become.

From THE POETRY OF ROBERT FROST, EDITED BY EDWARD CONNERY LATHEM, Copyright 1942 by Robert Frost, © 1970 by Lesley Frost Ballentine, © 1969 by Henry Holt & Co., Inc. Reprinted by permission of Henry Holt & Co., Inc.

Part One

Overview
of
Problems,
Issues
and
Prospects

1

Closing the Gap: Generating Opportunities for Minority Nurses in American Health Care

Hattie Bessent,
EdD, RN, FAAN

The Institute of Medicine has initiated a call for a more systematic and sustained effort to ensure the continuous flow of ethnic minority students qualified to choose careers in the health professions. The purpose of this volume is to respond to this initiative by providing insights into some of the theoretical and practical issues involved in accomplishing this goal. These combined experiences represent a wealth of practical and professional knowledge from experts who are committed to this endeavor that underpins the proposals and recommendations offered below.

In its report *Balancing the Scales of Opportunity in Health Care: Ensuring Racial and Ethnic Diversity in the Health Professions* (1994) the institute declared, "Some of the most serious deficiencies in our current health care enterprise are reflected in the growing disparity in health status between minority and majority populations." This observation takes on a more serious urgency when we consider demographic projections for the 21st century. By the year 2000, ethnic minorities will constitute one-third of America's population, and will represent an even greater proportion of the work force by the year 2020. In many areas of the country, ethnic minorities will become the numerical majority in the next century. This is already the case in some border states such as California, Florida and Texas. The implications of these demographic trends for the work force for the next century are obvious. Therefore, it is especially important that we are cognizant of the shifting demographic trends and the training issues described below. During the next several years, national conversations and other forums will concern themselves with these issues. It is imperative that the development of a framework for viewing nursing within the broader context of the Institute of Medicine's discussion on ethnic diversity in the health professions begin. This framework should include the potential impact of health care restructuring of these populations from the standpoint of the professional care giver, trainer, and the targeted populations they serve.

The Institute of Medicine's initiative begins at a time when institutions of higher education are facing declining resources, an increasingly rapid rate of knowledge explosion, a greater emphasis on globalization and internationalism, and an increased dependency on more sophisticated and costly technology. These trends will complicate to our efforts. Further complications will result from the unknowns associated with managed care. On the positive side, however, there are increasing pressures to achieve an accommodation and respect for multi-ethnicity, for multiculturalism in curriculum, and personnel matters. As nursing positions itself to increase its influence in the health care debate, we must ensure that it commits to a work force that utilizes the richness of our nation's diversity. The challenge is now before us.

Diversity

We begin with the simple observation that diversity is a strength. From a socio-biological perspective, the human species survives because the threats to any one population is mitigated by admixture. Diversity expands the adaptive capability of the human species. The principle holds as well in the socio-cultural environment in which individual complexity buffers external threats. The United States began an imperfect experiment that promoted cultural homogeneity. From its beginning, the United States has struggled with the mystery of diversity and the problems of difference. To this day, we continue to experience the polarities of strength and tension as we fumble with the contrasting ideologies of homogeneity and multiculturalism, color-blindness, and color-sensitivity or acceptance. Democracy, under the banner of *E Pluribus Unum,* has never fully resolved the issue of who constituted a citizen. Early emphasis in the evolving United States of America focused on cultural homogeneity through the "melting pot" phenomenon. This thrust had its roots in efforts to establish a single national language. Benjamin Franklin, for example, was reportedly suspicious of any tongue other than English and wanted the schools to wean the Pennsylvania Dutch from their foreign accents. It was important that all newcomers be "Americanized." Immigrants were asked to forsake their cultural and ethnic identities and become assimilated into the mainstream. Restrictive immigration screening that often employed psychological tests, contributed to the sorting out of acceptable and unacceptable persons. Further, the educational system was enlisted as a vehicle or instrument for shaping and preserving cultural homogeneity.

At the turn of the century, educator Ellwood Cubberley (1909) summarized the central role of education in the process of acculturation. Cubberley admonished schools to assimilate people of color as a part of America, to implant in their children, so far as can be done, the Anglo-Saxon conception of righteousness, law, order, and popular government, and to awaken in them reverence for democratic institutions. Racist ideology, however, contradicted this thesis in that people of color were never fully allowed to participate in the institutional life of America. The march of history, immigration, and accompanying demographic changes have proven to be stronger forces than the institutional drive for cultural homogeneity. Michael Lind's (1995) provocative essay on this history characterized these shifts in the American soil as Anglo-America to Euro-America to Multicultural-America. His commentary and the volatility of today's cultural conflict challenge us to build bridges and find common ground (unity in diversity) for a 21st century America that promises dramatic shifts in the proportionality of ethnic groups, and other lifestyle changes in our population and institutions. The melting pot ideology has given way to the garden salad or mosaic metaphor. The premise of a multicultural or pluralistic society gains momentum with each passing day. The National Coalition for Pluralism defines pluralism as a state of equal co-existence in a mutually supportive relationship within the boundaries or framework of one nation of people of diverse cultures.

In this chapter, I will summarize some of the issues that may affect the successful recruitment of ethnic and racial minority students to nursing training programs. I will next consider some of the general principles that recruitment, admissions, retention, and graduation should entail. Finally, I will close by issuing a challenge to the field, which will be taken up in the chapters contained in this monograph.

As we began the second half of the 19th century, there was a harbinger of progress in the public landscape of America. On May 17, 1954, in the *Brown v. Board of Education of Topeka* decision, the United States Supreme Court ruled that racial segregation in America's schools was unconstitutional.

> Separate educational facilities are inherently unequal. Therefore we hold that the plaintiffs and others similarly situated for whom actions have been brought are, by reason of the segregation complained of, deprived of the equal protection of the laws guaranteed by the fourteenth amendment.

The Court cited social science research by, among others, Kenneth and Mamie Clark (1947), which showed that racial segregation had deleterious effects on the emotional well being of young Black children. The Court ruled that whatever authority the doctrine of "separate but equal" was based on in the *Plessy v. Ferguson* decision of 1896, "modern authority" (social science research) declares that separate is inherently unequal. This promise for change turned out to be a promissory note that we are still waiting to collect on.

The 1960s offered another promise of racial equality based on individual character not skin color. The Civil Rights Act of 1964 is widely hailed as the most important legislation on behalf of racial and ethnic opportunity of this century (King and Quick 1965). The act contained 11 titles which spelled out the intent of Congress and the actionable abridgments of civil rights. Important to our concern with educational opportunities is Title VII, which states in section 703, paragraph (a), that it would be unlawful for an employer to "fail or refuse to hire or to discharge any individual or otherwise discriminate against any individual with respect to his compensation, terms, conditions, or privileges of employment, because of such individual's race, color, sex, or national origin," and it would similarly be unlawful to ". . . limit, segregate, or classify . . . employees in any way which would deprive . . . an individual of employment opportunities. . . ." Paragraph (d) extended these prohibitions to training programs. Title VI succinctly made the same point:

> No person in the United States shall, on the ground of race, color, or national origin, be excluded from participation in, be denied benefits of, or be subjected to discrimination under any program or activity receiving financial assistance [from the federal government]." (§601)

Thus, it would seem, the Civil Rights Act of 1964 set the stage for an increase in opportunities for racial groups, including the training of persons for health care professions.

In 1972, Allan Bakke applied to the Medical School at the University of California at Davis and was rejected. He was again rejected in 1974. Since there were 10 slots available but 16 had been reserved for African American, Latino, and American Indian applicants, Bakke felt that his rights were violated (Eastland and Bennett 1979). The decision was handed down on June 18, 1978, which by a 5-4 vote "affirmed" the illegality of the separate admissions program for ethnic/racial minority students. But in a separate 5-4 opinion, the Court "reversed" the California ruling that differences in race or color were neither significant or relevant and that people should be treated without regard to either. The Court, under the pen of Justice Brennen, agreed that the Fourteenth Amendment clause guaranteeing equal protection did not suggest or imply that a "colorblind" standard be employed in judging fairness. In fact, Justice Brennen went on to acknowledge an apparent paradox about race.

> A race-conscious remedy [is necessary to achieve a fully integrated society . . . [and] if ways are not found to remedy [under-representation of minorities in the professions] the country can never achieve . . . a society that is *not* race-conscious. . . . *In order to get beyond racism, we must first take account of race.*

It is ironic that Title VI of the 1964 Civil Rights Act, which seemed to promise so many opportunities for people of color, was used to invalidate a program that sought to make up for centuries of discrimination. More recently, in *Hopwood v. Texas,* even the Bakke decision support of race criteria for admissions was ruled inappropriate. Although this decision was limited to the Fifth Circuit, many educational programs have already rejected race-based admissions decisions. Realists show that the enrollment of African Americans and Latinos in public colleges and universities of Texas have declined by between 50 percent and 80 percent.

So, the 1970s and 1980s have produced a battleground in which remedies to the historical rejection of persons of color in educational settings, has been muted by legal attacks based on principles of individual freedom. There appears to be a recurring affect on these assaults on recruitment and admissions of people of color in nursing. For example, in 1996, the ten highest rated schools of nursing in the United States enrolled 7,897 students, among which were 494 (6.3 percent) African American students (Hines 1996). The number of African American faculty in those same schools was 44 (6.0 percent). Neither the students nor the faculty that teaches them are representative either of the population of the U. S., or the health care needs of these communities. We've come a modest way and have a long way to go.

In spite of the desire to integrate education in America, it appears that this has not happened in the nursing profession (Hines 1989). Why have efforts to recruit and train people of color for nursing professions been so slow? First, opening up of graduate schools of nursing has been very slow. By 1920, there were 36 schools of nursing for African Americans (Carnegie 1986). In 1996, as we noted earlier, 494 African American students were enrolled in the top 10 predominantly White nursing schools (Hines 1996). In that same year, 3,606 were enrolled in the top 10 Black nursing schools. When compared to enrollment in undergraduate schools generally, this is a decidedly more segregated representation than college. Where it is estimated that only 35 percent of all African American students attend predominantly Black colleges and universities.

In 1994, the National League for Nursing reported that over the last five years, the picture for minority graduation from nursing programs has been embarrassing. Graduations of minority students from all programs declined during this period from 14 percent to 12.7 percent. In 1993, African American students accounted for 6.8 percent and Hispanic students 2.6 percent of the graduations from all generic nursing programs (Moccia 1994).

This is quite discomforting since the Division of Nursing 1992 National Sample Survey reports there are more than 2 million nurses in the U.S.: 4 percent African American or 90,611; 1.4 percent Hispanics or 30,441; 3.4 percent Asian Pacific Islander or 75,785 and 0.4 percent American Indian/Alaskan Native or 9,998 (Division of Nursing 1992).

As historically White colleges and universities opened their doors to students of color, so too have the professions of prestige—medicine, business and law. Since nursing training can occur at the baccalaureate level, and other professions require advanced degrees, it may be that more and more students of color have sought training in other professional spheres. The result of this trend is that those who seek nursing careers remain at historically Black colleges and universities where training is available and they are accepted. For example, the nursing school at the University of Maryland at Baltimore counted 162 Black students among their 1,553 students in 1996, or 10.4 percent (Hines 1996). Yet, the University of Maryland at Baltimore medical school counted 25 African American students among their 175 students or 14.2 percent.

The fact is, nurses of color are sorely needed in America, and there are too few of them. Our predominantly Black colleges and universities still produce the vast majority of trained RNs, and have almost no input into the training of doctoral level nurses. With our increasingly diverse society, and the evidence that cultural factors influence health care utilization as well as means of access, failure in the training of nurses of color will translate to failure to deliver effective health care to our ethnic and racial minority citizens.

Recruiting, Admitting and Graduating Nurses of Color

To effectively recruit students of color for careers in nursing requites a varied, multi-tiered approach (Green 1989). Opportunities must be known, openness of training institutions must be real, and continuing mentoring and follow-up is needed to see students through to graduation. No one person can do all of this. No one strategy is sufficient to accomplish the goal. Let's briefly consider, in turn, the three major aspects of growing the pool of nurses of color in American health care—Recruitment, Retention and Graduation.

Recruitment

While everyone must be on board with the goal of increasing the representation of ethnic/racial minority students, the recruitment plan must be organized and funded. This means you need someone who has the responsibility of improving the numbers of students applying and being admitted. As with so many other training areas, if you wait passively for applicants, you will not be able to grow the pool. The pool is fed by a pipeline that needs to be nurtured. Many national programs acknowledge that beginning at an early age is crucial to success. The entering college student is giving way to the high school student who, in turn, is passed by for elementary school students as targets for recruitment. The return on dollar invested is a critical issue and goès down dramatically in the short run as you target younger and younger potential students. However, in the long run, this investment will pay off as nursing will achieve great prominence in the minds of young people as they mature and begin making plans for college and career.

A variety of ways to recruit students is possible. Recruiters, coordinated by the Minority Recruitment Office, travel to cities across the country making presentations to high schools and colleges. Exchange programs with faculty at institutions with large minority populations are another way to gain visibility. Developing sister school programs with high schools where students are able to come to campus and become involved in campus activities related to nursing. These early experiences not only increase the chances that young students will consider nursing, but put a given school in a prime position to recruit them.

Career days, regional conferences and such public events are all part of the mix of activities one should consider. But one thing is sure, recruiting will not be successful if students are not prepared to be successful in their studies. Successfully recruiting a large number of students who fail to complete the program is not much success. So, as part of the recruitment strategy, helping to shore up training programs in schools from which applicants come is an important idea. Maintaining ongoing relationships with high school and college programs is very useful.

Recruitment is incomplete and ultimately a failure if qualified students do not gain admission, so let's turn to admission.

Admission

Acquiring a student that the school has recruited is not always easy, but is an important part of closing the deal. There are two sides to the admission decision, yours and theirs. Too often, programs only think of whether the student they are considering can do the job, has what it takes, and so forth. This is certainly an important decision. Colleges must understand that applicants usually have alternatives. What does the school have to offer this applicant? Having a program with some prestige is a nice beginning, but what more? I have spoken with many parents of talented students of color and they have a large choice of programs. Why should they come to your program?

Too often, programs believe they are doing the student a favor by admitting them. Or, they may think they are doing their school a favor by increasing the number of students of color, showing they are on target. But it is crucial to think about what you have to offer and why a student is better off coming to your program. Consider that the student is from a cultural background that is important to him or her. Further, consider that they will want to use their training in some way that benefits people from their communities. Will you provide them with the skills to do that? Will they be able to develop their professional skills in relation to the kinds of problems they will likely encounter in their practicing environment? If you cannot offer them any specialized experience or context based skills, then perhaps they will not choose your program.

Now, how rigidly do schools apply their criteria for admission? Are Graduate Record Examination (GRE) scores over 1200 and GPAs over 3.5 cutoffs? Standardized or criterion measures should be considered carefully against the range of preparation and potential the students bring. Being flexible and sensitive to the measures that matter in a student's profile is important. What markers of motivation do you see? Are there indications that students have gone out of their way to learn something or have taken advantage of opportunities that became available to enhance their skills? How prepared are they for knowing what your program has to offer? Admissions programs can develop a list of intangibles to help in making good admissions decisions.

It is important that admissions be in tune with recruitment. The recruiter must have some say in admissions, and should be included in the process in a major way. Now if you are successful in recruiting and admitting students of color, you must graduate them or it is for naught.

Retention and Graduation

The simplest standard of success is graduation, probably more so than recruitment. In my judgment, a program that admits 25 students and graduates five is not as good as one that admits and graduates five. To successfully graduate students of color, you must be sure that they are involved in the program's formal and informal processes. Often the informal activities—breakfasts at a faculty member's house, party for a distinguished visitor, workshops for grant writing, or leadership forums—provide an opportunity to network. I should note here that the Kellogg leadership project that I ran for several years made many of these informal activities in nursing schools, formal activities in my project. The result is that many of these students, some of which had earned their doctoral degrees, learned further how to find and take advantage of opportunities for professional development and growth. Faculty and staff must be sure that students of color are not left out of these informal training opportunities. A degree is a symbol of completion, but skills, knowledge, self-confidence, and career success are much more important measures of training.

Mentoring

Finally, students need to have mentors. This is a conclusion of the Institute of Medicine report and one of the most significant aspects of success. Mentors are not only major professors, research advisors or department heads. Mentors are people who help the student develop and grow. The mentor helps them make decisions, as their growth progresses, and provides constant feedback and support. A mentor may also play a critical role as a reality check. Mentors keep a student focused. A program must be sure that a student has a mentor, or provide one as needed.

A mentor is viewed by Megel (1985) as a colleague or a sponsor. Nursing takes the view of mentoring as being a supportive relationship that requires the mentor to be cognitively and emotionally involved in all facets of the mentee's life (Campbell-Heider 1986; Fields 1991; Lev,

Souder, and Topp 1990; Kelly 1978; May, et al. 1982; Megel 1985; Williams and Blackburn 1988).

Because racism is such a constant, everyday experience for African Americans (Boyd-Franklin 1989; Felder 1992; Grier and Cobbs 1968; Pierce 1975) suggests having a conversation about race at the beginning of the relationship. Color-blindness is no virtue if it means denial of differences in experience and culture. These differences are not genetic, nor do they represent a hierarchy of superior and inferior qualities, but to ignore the formative influence of substantial differences in history and social existence is a great error (Thomas and Sillen 1974, 58).

Hardy (1989) feels color-blindness is not the answer to establishing an honest relationship with a person of color. The mentee must possess a healthy amount of paranoia. Grier and Cobbs (1968) call this type of paranoia as healthy, cultural paranoia (Grier and Cobbs 1968, 161). They view the cultural paranoia as a coping strategy that allows the minority person to develop trusting relationships with majority members while protecting self against betrayal.

Studies have shown that the success for minority groups and disadvantaged students is positively related to the number of faculty role models and support services available (Tucker-Allen 1992). Tucker-Allen (1992) also pointed out that several studies have revealed a relationship between the number of Black faculty at predominantly White institutions and recruitment, admission, and graduation of Black students (Tucker-Allen 1992, 89).

If nursing is to increase the number of minorities in nursing from 7 percent of 2 million registered nurses in the United States (Tucker-Allen 1991), programs to prepare minority nurses at the highest educational levels are needed. Blank and Slipp (1994) identified some strategies that may be used by the mentee and the mentor to enhance the success of the mentee.

Key Strategies for Mentees

- Never assume that the environment is completely hostile.
- Find a mentor who is in the dominant group in the setting.
- Recognize that because of your group identity, you have something distinctive and important to offer.
- Don't allow yourself always to be the representative of your group.
- Emphasize what you have in common with your mentor and the other students.
- Realize that not every slight or misunderstanding is necessarily racist, sexist or discriminatory.
- Recognize clearly sexist, racist, and other discriminatory or stereotypic remarks or behavior.
- Ask for what you want.

- Be aware of your own stereotypes of others.
- Gain visibility in the school.
- Try to learn and understand from the perspectives of others.
- Have a vision for yourself.

Key Strategies for Mentors

- Approach every student as an individual.
- Recognize and confront the issue of discomfort—your own and others in dealing with a minority student.
- Appreciate and utilize the different perspectives and styles of minority students.
- Convey clearly your expectations for minority students, while at the same time recognizing and contextualizing their individual needs.
- Provide feedback often and equally to your mentees.
- Openly support the competencies and contributions of the students in the group.
- Be aware of subtle and systemic institutional discrimination—intentional or unintentional—that limits opportunities for minority students fellows.
- Confront racist, sexist, or other stereotypic or invidious individual and institutional discriminatory behavior.
- Don't assume that all minority students will have the same skills, beliefs, or behaviors.
- Finally, understand that it is the mentor who ultimately holds the key for developing the full potential of the minority students.

The literature consistently reveals that when a positive, open, honest interpersonal relationship exists between the mentee and the mentor, the productivity of the mentee is assured (Outlaw 1993).

This brief overview of issues related to the successful recruitment, admission, retention and graduation of students of color will be recurring themes in the chapters that follow. These chapters will provide insight into the cultural variations that affect how one must go about recruiting students. They will provide data illustrating our current state, some strategies for making progress, and some specific issues that stand as barriers along the way. These approaches are informed by multiple disciplines from sociology to philosophy, anthropology, psychology, social work, and nursing. I am confident that upon reading this monograph, you will have a great deal of knowledge, perspective, data and proposals that can be utilized in admissions programs. The ultimate goal of increasing the representation of nurses of color in the health care system in America is an important objective that I believe we all share.

The overall purpose of the examination of the participation of minorities in nursing was to develop a framework for viewing nursing in a broader context than that delineated in the Institute of Medicine study on ensuring racial and ethnic diversity in the health professions. Specifically, I intended to develop future-oriented strategies that provide an action agenda for nursing that is responsive to the realities of the late '90s. Also, I examined aspects of professional development that affect underrepresented minorities in nursing.

Minority nurses are defined in this manuscript as African American, Asian, Hispanic and Native American. Race is distinguished for human populations as a more or less distinct group identified by genetically transmitted physical characteristics. Culture is defined as the totality of socially transmitted behavior patterns, arts, beliefs, institutions and all other products of human work and thought typical of a population or community at a given time. Ethnicity relates to a religious, racial, national, or cultural group. I used a number of sources in a variety of fields in an effort to provide a thorough look at processes that would result in an increase of ethnic minorities in the field of nursing.

Manuscripts were requested from reputable individuals in their fields. Contributors were chosen based on their knowledge, advocacy, leadership, and contributions to enhancing the inclusion of minorities in higher education and their commitment to increasing the number of minority nurses with baccalaureate and graduate degrees. The manuscripts cover several pertinent issues relevant to solving the problem of the underrepresentation of minority nurses. The issue of affirmative action and the qualification dilemma of individuals interested in nursing; the experience of minorities in higher education as an example of what they may encounter in academic programs; cultural dimensions specific to minority groups; attitudes, beliefs and behaviors; philosophical, psychological, sociological, and economic issues in nursing as it relates to minorities.

Workshops were held with a group of experts who represented the professions of nursing, medicine, psychology, sociology, education and economics. They participated in the identification of strategies for the recruitment, retention, and graduation of minority nurses. Those strategies for which there was 90 percent agreement were ranked by a panel of experts and a sample of fellows.

A panel of 10 experts ranked each of the strategies with one being the highest rank and the most important. A convenience sample of 10 former fellows of the American Nurses Association Minority Fellows program also ranked the strategies in the same manner based on importance.

Questionnaires were mailed to the deans of nursing programs in select institutions in the United States. The deans were assured anonymity if they participated. The report of that survey appears in Chapter III. Specific models on recruitment, retention and graduation for minority nurses were sought from various sources. Few, if any models have been developed, as I received no responses. However, I am aware of programs designed to recruit minority students. Two sets of definitive plans for increasing diversity, one set of goals and objectives for diversity and a description of a mentoring program were received.

14

Generating Opportunities
for Minority Nurses

I visited 10 university nursing programs located in the northeast, midwest, northwest, southeast, and southwest of this country. Focus groups consisting of an average of 12 students were held at each of the institutions. A meeting with select faculty and/or staff and administrators was held at most of the institutions. Twenty of the students who attended the focus groups also provided written information about recruiting, retention and graduating minorities. Some of the relevant information obtained in the focus groups appears in Chapter XII where specific strategies are discussed. Institutions were selected based on availability.

As so often in our collective history, we stand again at a crossroads in health care employment and specifically in nursing education. The choices seem clear. Do we continue along a path that results de facto in a health and education system largely devoid of participation by major segments of our population? The issue transcends "moral" imperatives and instead goes to the heart of what constitutes quality health care and education. Participation and access on the part of ethnic communities are benchmarks of quality health care and of education.

The alternative to the current picture is to go forward collectively by encouraging nursing programs to implement effective steps for minority participation discussed throughout this volume. The fact that efforts under the traditional rubric of affirmative action are under attack at this juncture in our history represents a challenge technically in terms of the dismembering of programs and regulations. However, the challenge can be met by creative programmatic efforts to bring increased numbers of the ethnic minority communities into participation in health and nursing education. As we have seen, there are effective strategies beginning with recruitment programs, retention programs, and programs to help the newly graduated transition into professional roles.

These programs can and have been implemented without creating a zero-sum situation among categories of students and professionals. Rather, movement toward the goal of increased opportunity for minority participation is an imperative in nursing education and in health care that is rooted in the mainstream ideals that formed our society, our collective culture, and our nation—which is surely in our collective self-interest. In reality, schools of nursing are in the unique position of serving as the effective model for movement toward increased minority participation and for demonstrating strategies by which we can move forward together toward a more effective, comprehensive, and responsive health and education system for all of our population.

Living one's life, which is often best understood through a rear view mirror, looking back, gives us increments of wisdom for safe keeping. Looking back at the history of nursing in the United States, one cannot fail to notice that through all the stresses and vagaries, the slights and the dismissals, a golden thread of fidelity has endured. We have in the main held fast to our highest values, our belief in ourselves as persons who do good, our role as healers. This has historically best been expressed with the phrase one patient, one family, one group, one community. As we move into our evolutionary challenge, our call to heightened consciousness, we may find that fidelity once more tested, this time in a new and larger crucible, one that calls on us not only to serve as healers in the microcosm of daily practice but also in some larger sense, to take our place as healers of the fractures and dislocations of a world community struggling to bridge the small and large differences that keep us separate, uncommunicative, untouchable. Healing the global community asks a good deal more of us, and thus brings forth a good deal more of our goodness. It is ultimately in our self-interest to notice this. It is also possible that we might notice in our response to this call that our self-interest is inextricably bound up with the interest of all others, that a global community already exists, eager for the responsive touch of nursing's healing wisdom and traditions. Responding to this challenge, bringing that healing process forward, we may indeed discover that we have thereby healed our own broken selves.

However, simply believing it is important is not enough. The Institute of Medicine report lauded our efforts to improve the representation and inclusion of persons of color in the health professions, but pronounced the job unfinished. While I am sure people agree with the goal, we must dedicate ourselves to success. We must understand the principles of diversity and make them our own. We must understand that the inclusion of diverse peoples in our health care system will improve the delivery of health care to our most needy citizens. Nurses have a vital role to play in this. I sincerely hope that this monograph will help move us along the path to a better society and a healthier society. I close this chapter with a vision from James Jones (1997) who ends his prejudice and racism with this challenge:

> Two paths stand before us. One, motivated by the best sense of liberty, equality and fraternity, moves us forward in the experiment in creating a more perfect union. A second fueled by fear, self-interest, ignorance, and mistrust, turns us backward, and diverts us from the struggle toward tolerance and perfection. Our diversity comes from different origins, experiences and goals. Our best possible selves as a nation and a people will be determined by the path we choose. (p. 537)

References

Bakke v. Board of Regents State of California, United States Supreme Court, 1978.

Bakke v. Board of Regents State of California, United States Supreme Court, 1985.

Blank, R., and S. Slipp. 1994. *Voices of diversity: Real people talk about problems and solutions in a workplace where everyone is not alike.* New York: American Management Association.

Boyd-Franklin, N. 1989. *Black families in therapy: A multisystem approach.* New York: Guilford Press.

Brown v. Board of Education of Topeka, United States Supreme Court, 1954.

Campbell-Heider, N. 1986. Do nurses need mentors? *Image: Journal of Nursing Scholarship* 18: 110–113.

Carnegie, E. 1986. *The path we tread: Blacks in nursing, 1854–1984.* Philadelphia: J.B. Lippincott.

Clark, K. B., and M. Clark. 1947. Racial identification and preference in Negro children. In *Readings in social psychology*, edited by T.M. Newcomb and E. L. Hartley. New York: Holt.

Cubberley, E.P. 1909. *Changing conceptions of education.* Boston: Houghton Mifflin.

Division of Nursing. 1992. 1992 National Sample Survey of Registered Nurses. Rockville, MD: Health Resources and Services Administration.

Division of Nursing. 1996. *Advance notes from the national sample survey of registered nurses.* Rockville, MD: Health Resources and Services Administration.

Eastland, T., and W.J. Bennett. 1979. *Counting by race: Equality from the founding fathers to Bakke and Weber.* New York: Basic Books.

Felder, E. 1992. Meeting the challenge of mentoring—African American nursing faculty: A strategy for professional development. *The Association of Black Nursing Faculty Journal* 3: 86–88.

Fields, W. 1991. Mentoring in nursing: A historical approach. *Nursing Outlook* 39: 257–261.

Green, M.F. 1989. *Minorities on campus: A handbook for enhancing diversity.* Washington, DC: American Council on Education.

Grier, W., and P. Cobbs. 1968. *Black rage.* New York: Basic Books.

Hardy, K. 1989. The theoretical myth of sameness: A critical issue in family therapy training and treatment. In *Minorities and family therapy*, edited by G. Saba, B. Karrer, and K. Hardy. New York: Haworth Press.

Hines, D.C. 1989. *Black women in white: Racial conflict and cooperation in the nursing profession.* Bloomington, IN: Indiana University Press.

Hines, D.C. 1996. The state of African Americans in nursing education. *Journal of Blacks in Higher Education* (Autumn): 52–54.

Jones, J.M. 1997. *Prejudice and racism* 2nd Ed. New York: McGraw-Hill.

Kelly, L. 1978. Power guide—The mentor relationship. *Nursing Outlook* 26: 339.

King, D.B., and C.Q. Quick, eds. 1965. *Legal aspects of the civil rights movement.* Detroit: Wayne State University Press.

Lev, E., E. Souder, and R. Topp. 1990. The postdoctoral fellowship experience. *Image: Journal of Nursing Scholarship* 22: 116–120.

Lewin, M., and B. Rice, B. eds. 1994. *Balancing the scales of opportunity in health care: Ensuring racial and ethnic diversity in the health professions.* Washington, DC: National Academy Press.

Lind, M. 1995. *The next American nation: The new nationalism and the fourth American revolution.* New York: Free Press.

May, K., A. Meleis, and P. Winstead-Fry. 1982. Mentorship for scholarship: Opportunities and dilemmas. *Nursing Outlook* 30: 22–28

Megel, M. 1985. New faculty in nursing: Socialization and the role of the mentors. *Journal of Nursing Education* 24: 303–306.

Moccia, Patricia. 1994. Trends in Contemporary Nursing Education. Nursing Data Source. New York: NLN Press.

Outlaw, F. 1993. Stress and coping: The influence of racism on the cognitive appraisal processing of African Americans. *Issues in Mental Health Nursing* 14: 339–409.

Pierce, C. 1975. The mundane extreme environmental stress: The case of Black families in White America. In *Learning disabilities: Issues and recommendations for research*, edited by S. G. Brainard. Washington, DC: Institute of Education.

Thomas, A., and S. Sillen. 1974. *Racism and psychiatry*. New Jersey: Citadel.

Tucker-Allen, S. 1991. Minority student nurses' perceptions of their educational program. *The Association of Black Nursing Faculty Journal* 2: 59–63.

Tucker-Allen, S. 1992. Mentoring role of black nursing faculty members. *The Association of Black Nursing Faculty Journal* 3: 89–92.

Williams, R., and R. Blackburn. 1988. Mentoring and junior faculty productivity. *Journal of Nursing Education* 27: 204–209.

2 Ensuring Ethnic and Racial Diversity in Nursing

Juanita W. Fleming, PhD, RN, FAAN

Two of the ten policy issues for higher education in 1997 and 1998 are affirmative action and health care system changes (Association of Governing Boards of Universities and Colleges 1997, 5). Court cases and other challenges to affirmative action may be the focus of attention for college and university officials. The transformation in the delivery and financing of health care which is occurring in the United States of America has implications for practice, research and the education of health professionals.

Another fundamental transformation occurring in America is the ethnic/ racial make-up of its people. At the turn of the century, one in every four Americans will be Black, Hispanic, Middle Eastern or Asian (Cetron and Davis 1989). The large number of non-European Americans is changing the ethnic and political character of the country. The ethnic/racial make up of the population and the transition of the health care system have implications for changes in the labor market for health professionals and particularly for nurses. As a result of these transformations, the curricula which are designed to prepare health care professionals both at the undergraduate level and graduate level will evolve. More curricula will likely include cultural content and a greater emphasis placed on science, mathematics and technology (National Academy of Sciences et.al 1997, 2). Direct experiences with methods and processes probably will be included in curricula. Ensuring ethnic and racial diversity in nursing and taking advantage of information technologies as we move into the twenty-first century are worthwhile goals.

In spite of laudable efforts, minorities in nursing and other health professionals continue to be marginalized, in that they remain underrepresented in leadership roles. A number of foundations, corporations, governmental agencies, professional organizations and universities have, and are engaging in, a discourse on diversity. The changing demographic projections are a powerful stimulus for this discourse. It should, however, be noted that the demographic configurations alone are not enough if our society is to benefit. A combination of strategies which will enable society to expand the participation of diverse groups in meeting the needs, particularly health care needs, of society seem warranted. The urgency to redress increasing the number of minority health professionals was inherent in a study done by the Institute of Medicine. In an effort to address this concern an Institute of Medicine committee was charged with developing a future-oriented research and strategic action plan. The committee focused on multiple aspects of professional development such as education, academic achievement, opportunity and mentoring that affect participation of underrepresented minorities in the health professions. Minorities were defined as African Americans, Hispanics and Native Americans for the Institute of Medicine project. These groups were found to be markedly underrepresented in the health professions.

The committee considered the effect of the increasing diversity of the U.S. population and the need to improve health services for minorities, while examining potential implications for the nation's future workforce. Major findings focused on systemic, integrated interventions that could ensure a continuous pool of students-from elementary school to college to post graduate or professional school. The committee called for a more systematic, strategic and sustained effort to ensure the continuous flow of minority students qualified to choose careers in the health professions. A strong science and math foundation was encouraged. Educational institutions were urged to develop specific goals and implementation plans for inclusion and excellence. The committee advocated that diversity becomes prized as a resource characterized by genuine respect for students' varying backgrounds, talents and learning styles, and noted that the commitment to diversity must be associated with heightened sensitivity and respect for cultural differences. The committee believed that one approach—mentoring—was especially critical in helping minorities achieve their career goals and that it must be a structural component of programs dedicated to achieving a larger presence of minorities in the health professions (Lewin and Rice 1994). Based on its findings, the committee recommended six strategies to increase minority participation in the health professions.

The Institute of Medicine is commended for its foresight in addressing the underrepresentation of minorities in the health professions. The focus of the report, however, was on the discipline of medicine primarily, though other health professions were noted. As a result, "nursing and other health providers probably should extend the work of the committee by obtaining more definitive information about ensuring racial and ethnic diversity in their professions (Fleming 1995).

The health care system is being transformed to systems of integrated care that combine primary, community, specialty and hospital care for the population. Consequently, more definitive health related data are needed on African American, and especially on other minority populations. It would be particularly beneficial to gather information on Hispanics, considering the projected population trends. Such information may help substantiate the critical need to address underrepresentation of minorities in the health professions.

Experts realize there is room for improvement. The report brought many significant and challenging issues to light. For example, there are several reasons why ensuring a balance of opportunities for minorities in health care is worthwhile to society. "First, in order to address the multiple health problems our country faces, it seems reasonable that all facets of the society—regardless of their race or ethnic group—should be involved in bringing about solutions. Second, the United States is not isolated. Because it functions as a part of the global community, the U.S. will benefit more in interactions with other nations if its representatives include individuals from various ethnic and racial groups. Third, it is difficult for a nation to model behavior that is not practiced or to influence other nations to make changes that it is not willing to make itself" (Fleming 1995)

Democracy and Diversity

The concept of democracy implies that human beings have equal value, deserve equal respect and should be given equal opportunity to fully participate in the life and direction of the society. The concept of diversity refers to the variety created in society by the presence of different points of view and ways of making meaning which generally flow from the influence of different cultural and religious heritages, from the differences in how we socialize people and from the differences that emerge from class, age and developed ability (AACU 1995, XX).

The Association of American Universities, a consortium of sixty-two leading universities in the nation, believe that students benefit significantly from education that takes place in diverse settings. It is recognized that to prepare students for life in the twenty-first century, they will need to encounter and learn from others who have background and characteristics different from their own.

From the founding of the United States until well into the twentieth century, historical records reflect racial stigmatization against non-white groups. The major higher education institutions have played a distinct role in the legacy of how the nation has treated its minorities. Changes in the racial and ethnic composition of the faculty and student bodies are emerging. Almost all campuses now see education of a diverse citizenry as integral to their missions of public leadership and service (AACU 1995, XX). Our university campuses will become more inclusive if they continue to broaden the understanding of the importance of a diverse democracy. The academy has become the testing grounds for diversity and possibilities of American pluralism. The university campuses are the sites for intercultural negotiation. Higher education's unique mission to expand human knowledge in various disciplines is also challenged to create campuses in which all those who are participants are treated equitably, welcomed, valued and heard. Research about the effects of diversity in nursing education and practice will likely contribute to how diversity initiatives impact learning and practice. The impact and importance of the expansion of knowledge, the effect of diversity on practice and the development of inclusive learning environments is critical.

Nursing and Diversity

The profession of nursing will need to take seriously the concept of diversity in the recruitment, enrollment, retention, education and graduation of students. Diversity is an important issue because it helps us recognize the humanness of all people. Further, the health of minorities and the delivery of health care to them in various practice settings is a critical issue. Not only is it an issue in terms of preparation of the nurses, but in terms of the complexity of care. Many minorities make up high risk population groups. A large number of them are poor and are not accessing the health care delivery system effectively. The prediction that 85 percent of those entering the workforce in 2000 will be women and minorities and that there will be a large increase of minority populations strongly suggests the importance of preparing health professionals who are able to help provide competent health care for all of those in our society who need it. A National Sample Survey of registered nurses revealed that:

- the estimated number of individuals in the United States with current licenses to practice as registered nurses in March 1996 was 2,558,874. Of these, 82.7 percent, or 2,115,815 were employed in nursing,
- about 10 percent, or 246,363 out of the 2,558,874, came from racial/ethnic minority background. An estimated 107,527 (4.2 percent) were Black (non-Hispanic); 86,434 (3.4 percent) were Asian/Pacific Islanders; 40,559 (1.6 percent) were Hispanics, and 11,843 (.5 percent) were American Indian/Alaskan Native,
- the average age of all the registered nurses was 44.3 years. Among those who were employed in nursing, the average age was 42.3 years,
- among the 2,115,815 employed registered nurses, 58.4 percent had less than a baccalaureate degree as their highest nursing-related educational preparation; 502,959 had diplomas and 731,613, an associate degree. An estimated 672,914 (31.8 percent) of the employed registered nurses had a baccalaureate degree as their highest preparation. Those with master's degrees totaled 193,159 (9.1 percent) and those who were doctorally prepared accounted for 14,300 (.6 percent) of the total employed registered nurses, and
- sixty percent of the employed registered nurses, or 1,270,870, were working in a hospital setting. Seventeen percent, or

362,648, were working in a community of public health setting. Ambulatory care settings, including settings such as physician or nurse solo or group practices and health maintenance organizations, accounted for 8.5 percent or 178,930. Nursing homes or other extended care facilities were the employment settings for 170,856 registered nurses, or 8.1 percent of the total. The remaining employed registered nurses were working in other types of settings such as nursing education, national or state administrative offices or associations, insurance companies (Division of Nursing 1996).

Unlike many other health professions, entry into the practice of "professional" nursing may be through a diploma program, an associate degree program, baccalaureate degree program or in a few instances through a master's degree program. The growth in nursing has come primarily from the rapid expansion of two year associate degree programs. The bulk of registered nurses, as shown in the National Sample Survey of Registered Nurses, are from diploma and associate degree programs. This preparation does not adequately address the potential opportunity and enormous demands that are likely to be placed on nursing in the future. Advanced preparation through baccalaureate study and master's level degrees will permit the nursing professional to develop background and an experience base to operate more independently, work in community settings, more effectively manage the health of patients, and make an even more profound contribution to health care (Pew Health Professions Commission 1995. 49).

The dearth of minority role models in administration and the professorate in academia for minority students is a concern and reflects the need for more doctorally prepared minority nurses. The American Council on Education found very few persons of color in university-wide or senior level administrative positions and recommend that research universities examine their policies for achieving diversity in administrative appointments and to seek immediately increase the representation of persons of color in policy-making administrative positions. The American Council noted, too, that graduate students of color are an important resource in the effort to increase the pool of persons of color for the academy. The Council recommended "that foundations, alone or in a joint enterprise, provide multiple-year grants to identify a group of people (from diverse institutions) who have outstanding track records in attracting and training graduate students of color to permit them to enlarge and enhance their work. It would be most helpful if they also could be supported to develop junior faculty of color. In turn, these junior faculty members would work with, mentor, and support undergraduate students of color who are preparing for graduate studies and academic careers" (Knowles and Harleston 1997).

The Pew Profession Commission noted that many of the challenges from the emerging system of care will impact all health professions. Specific mention was made of the growth of the scientific base to accommodate the changes; more sharing of clinical training resources, more cross teaching by professional faculties, active modeling of effective team integration in the delivery of efficient, high quality care; and a commitment to ensuring the students trained represent the rich ethnic diversity of our society (Pew Health Professions Commission 1995, 49). Since a large number of nurses have less than a baccalaureate degree as their highest nursing related educational preparation, it seems reasonable to conclude that some of these are minority nurses. Fitzsimons and Kelley substantiate this conclusion for one group of minority nurses. They noted that in 1992, 11 percent of the African American students were enrolled in baccalaureate degree programs and 89 percent in A.D. and Diploma Programs (Fitzsimons and Kelley 1996, 2).

The critical point here is the dramatic need to prepare more minority nurses at levels that will enable them to function in the emerging health care system effectively. Those nurses who have less than baccalaureate degree preparation in nursing have been prepared primarily for jobs in hospitals rather than varied settings. As many hospitals downsize or close, more nurses will be providing services in a variety of settings including hospitals, clinics, nursing homes, physician practices, home health agencies, community service settings and urgent care centers. Some will be involved in innovative services which will broaden access to primary health care and preventable ambulatory care. The changing health care system suggests that the education of nurses will need to change in order to better prepare nurses to provide competent care to those who access any part of the integrated health care system.

Nursing like other health professions, as suggested in the Institute of Medicine Report, would benefit from a focus on systemic, integrated interventions that could ensure a continuous pool of students from elementary school to college to post graduate or professional schools. The cadre of nurses who completed any type of nursing program— licensed practical nurse, diploma or associate degree programs—and who have the ability might also be recruited, enrolled, retained and graduated from baccalaureate, masters and doctoral degree programs. Nursing needs to prepare more minorities at the baccalaureate and graduate levels so that they, too, can assume roles as practitioners, researchers and academicians in the emerging integrated health care system.

The dimensions in nursing which include culture are relevant to addressing issues that relate to diverse populations whether they are students, consumers of health care or professionals. The Institute of Medicine study provided the stimulus for an examination of factors that influence the underrepresentation of minorities with preparation at the baccalaureate and graduate levels in nursing. The American Nurses Foundation has invested in having a distinguished scholar implement this examination and develop strategies for exemplary means of ensuring that diversity will emerge. The hope is that these strategies will not only be good for the profession of nursing, but for other professionals as well.

References

Association of American Colleges and Universities (AACU). 1995. *The Drama of Diversity and Democracy: Higher Education and American Commitments.* Washington, DC: Association of American Colleges and Universities.

Association of Governing Boards of Universities and Colleges. 1997. *AGB Public Policy Paper Series* No. 97-1.

Cetron, M., and O. Davis. 1989. *American Renaissance.* New York: St. Martins Press.

Division of Nursing. 1996. *Advanced Notes from the National Sample Survey of Registered Nurses.* Rockville, MD: Health Resources and Services Administration.

Fitzsimons, V.M., and M.L. Kelley. 1996. *The Culture of Learning.* New York: NLN Press.

Fleming, J. 1995. Balancing the Scales of Opportunity in Health Care: Ensuring Racial and Ethnic Diversity in the Health Professions. *Health Care Trends and Transition* 6(4): 24–26, 28, 30, 32.

Knowles, M.F., B.W. Harleston 1997. *Achieving Diversity in the Professoriate: Challenges and Opportunities. A Report for the American Council on Education.* Washington, DC: American Council on Education.

Lewin, M, and B. Rice, eds. 1994. *Balancing the Scales of Opportunity in Health Care: Ensuring Racial and Ethnic Diversity in the Health Professions.* Washington, DC: National Academy Press.

National Academy of Sciences, National Academy of Engineering, Institute of Medicine, National Research Council. 1997. *Preparing for the 21st Century. The Education Imperative.* Washington, DC: National Research Council.

Pew Health Professions Commission. 1995. *Critical Challenges: Revitalizing the Health Professions for the Twenty-First Century (November). The Third Report of the Pew Health Professions Commission.*

3

Survey of Select Universities Regarding Recruitment, Enrollment, Retention, and Graduation of Minorities in Nursing

Hattie Bessent, EdD, RN, FAAN

There is evidence that there is concern about the participation of minorities in nursing (Lewin and Rice 1994; NLN 1990). Minorities appear to be seriously underrepresented at the baccalaureate, masters and doctoral levels. Further, in spite of declared interest in ethnic diversity in nursing, there has been little in the way of a systematic effort to correct the implicit underrepresentation.

One of the approaches used to examine the participation of minorities in nursing was to investigate the recruitment, enrollment, retention and graduation status of minorities in undergraduate and graduate programs in nursing.

Specific questions posed were:

1. What is the status of recruitment, enrollment, retention and graduation of minorities in undergraduate and graduate programs in nursing?
2. What are the barriers that mitigate against enrollment, retention and graduation of minorities in undergraduate and graduate programs in nursing?
3. What are the strategies, techniques and/or models being used to enhance enrollment, retention and graduation of minorities in undergraduate and graduate programs in nursing?
4. What are the issues associated with implementing strategies to admit, enroll, retain and graduate minorities?
5. Are there aspects on which there should be focus to enhance professional development among minorities in nursing?

This chapter describes a survey of a sample of the nation's major research universities and leading grantors of doctoral degrees. Using a stratified sampling technique, the sampled institutions were selected from a list of those major research institutions that offered a nursing program. The stratification assured that institutions were selected from the northeast, northwest, midwest, southeast and southwest. Sixty-two (62) institutions were selected. The assumptions made about the institutions were that the nation's major research universities and leading grantors of doctoral degrees would be the most likely institutions to 1.) have models or plans for addressing diversity; 2.) focus on recruitment, enrollment, retention and graduation of individuals from diverse groups; 3.) have resources to engage in innovative ways to recruit, enroll, retain and graduate individuals from diverse groups; and 4.) have strong campus wide leadership committed to diversity.

The assumptions are in keeping with the Association of American Colleges and Universities' National Diversity Initiative of 1993. The focus is on the educational mission in its largest social context. That mission is fostering social learning about diversity in the United States in relation to the nation's democratic aspiration and values (Lewin and Rice 1994). In its commitment to diversity, higher education assumes, both a distinctive responsibility and a precedent-setting challenge. Other institutions in society are also fostering diversity. Higher education, however, is uniquely positioned, by its mission, values, and dedication to learning, to foster and nourish the habits of heart and mind that Americans need to make diversity work in daily life. Institutions of higher education have an opportunity to help their campuses experience engagement across difference as a value and a public good.[2] Almost all campuses now see education of a diverse citizenry as an integral part of their mission of public leadership and service (Cetron 1989).

While I believe that diversity is a complex issue and broader than race and/or gender, the focus of this investigation is on minorities as defined by the Office of Civil Rights for students that are citizens, that is African Americans, Asians, Hispanics and Native Americans. Along with race and ethnicity, cultural differences among these groups were also a consideration.

Of the 62 mailed surveys, there were 33 responders. Three mailed follow-ups were sent to each of the institutions. One responder replied twice with identical information. One of the two surveys was discarded. The total number of responders to the survey was 32, 51.6 percent.

The survey was designed to elicit information on recruitment, enrollment, retention and graduation of minorities. Participants were assured that the information would be placed in the form of statistical summaries from which it would be impossible to identify any specific person or institution. The survey instrument appears in Appendix 1, and the summary tables discussed in the report appear in Appendix 2.

To determine if the questions were consistent, two different groups were asked to rate the questions to determine the level of difficulty an institution would experience in attempting to answer. There was 100 percent agreement on Part I. However, 50 percent or one-half believed that institutions would have difficulty answering Parts II, III and IV. While the groups felt the questions in Parts II, III and IV were important to ask, there was some concern about how valuable the information would be for generalization purposes, because of the variation that was likely to exist in the institutions. Nevertheless, the consensus was that some information might emerge that would be useful to include as exemplary for institutions and that would be worth sharing.

The instrument was judged to have face and content validity in that all of the items that were included in the final questionnaire were judged by experts to be acceptable and appropriate for obtaining accurate information about recruitment, enrollment, retention and graduation. The instrument was pilot tested for readability and clarity. Changes were made based on responses received from those who provided information.

Data Analysis

Due to positive skewness in the numerical response, the median of the responses were tabulated along with the means. This was seen as being useful in interpreting enrollment and degree counts for all students combined. Because of the varying sizes of the schools when tabulating minority student counts, the statistician also expressed the counts as relative frequencies (proportion of minority students). Tabulations were done both ways—frequency counts as well as relative frequency counts.

All of the schools except one had a doctoral program in nursing, four did not offer the baccalaureate degree in nursing and one did not offer a masters degree in nursing. This was taken into account in the tables on enrollment and degree counts. Rather than set the enrollment count equal to a zero for a school without a program, the statistician eliminated that school when computing the statistics for that level of students (e.g., undergraduates). Consequently, the number of responders in the enrollment count and degree count tables will not always be 32.

Some of the responders did not break down minority counts by gender, but instead supplied total counts combining both genders. This caused differences between the number of responders for counts by gender vs. counts based on both genders combined.

General Information

Enrollment

The overall mean number of students enrolled in the responding institutions is 675.2 with a mean of 68.7 for males and a mean of 606.5 for females [see Table 1A(1)]. For those programs with undergraduate programs, the median enrollment of students is 424 and the mean is 416.3. The median for those with masters programs is 211 and the mean is 234.1. For the programs offering doctoral programs, the median is 45.0 and the mean is 53.4. The other eleven programs such as specialty programs for nurse practitioners not necessarily leading to a degree, but certification, had a median enrollment of 34 and a mean enrollment of 56.4 [See Table 1A(2)]. Notice that of the total number of students enrolled in nursing degree programs, 55.9 percent are undergraduate students, 33.6 percent are masters degree students, 7.7 percent are doctoral degree students, and only 2.9 percent are students enrolled in other degree programs. Hence, even at major research universities, nursing enrollments are dominated by undergraduate students and masters degree students. Nursing programs are also dominated by female students since they account for 89.8 percent of the total enrollment in nursing.

Tables 1B(1) and 1B(2) provide the enrollment of African Americans, and the relative frequency percentage respectively. Tables 1B(3) and 1B(4) provide enrollment of Asians and the relative frequency percentage. Tables 1B(5) and 1B(6) provide the enrollment of Hispanics and the relative frequency percentages respectively. Tables 1B(7) and 1B(8) provide the enrollment of Native Americans and the relative frequency percentage. The median for the total enrollment of minorities is 71.00 and the mean is 91.25. See Table 1B(9) and 1B(10) for total enrollment and relative frequency percentage. On average, minority students account for 14.7 percent of the total enrollment in nursing degree programs. This varies by type of degree since on average 18.3 percent of undergraduate students are minorities, only 10.7 percent of masters students are minorities and 14.0 percent of doctoral students are minorities. This also varies among specific groups: 35.3 percent of minority students are African-Americans, 30.0 percent are Asians, 19.3 percent are Hispanic, and 15.3 percent are Native American. P<.05 level of confidence was set for testing significant differences. There is a significant difference in the enrollment of Native Americans, Asians and African Americans and a significant difference in the enrollment of Hispanics and African Americans. Fewer Native Americans than Asians or African Americans are enrolled in programs. Fewer Hispanics than African Americans are enrolled.

Degrees Awarded in the Last Five Years

Tables 1C(1) and 1C(2) provide the total number of degrees awarded in the last five years from the 32 institutions. The median of 1017.5 and mean of 1006.1 were awarded undergraduate, masters and doctoral degrees with the largest number as expected being the undergraduate degree. Tables 1D(3)-1D(8) provide the number of degrees awarded to minorities in the last five years. Tables 1D(9) and 1D(10) provide the total median 97.00 and mean 115.4 of degrees awarded to minorities in the last five years and the relative frequency for total minorities. There is no significant difference in the degrees awarded to Hispanics, Asians and African Americans, but there is a significant difference in those awarded to Native Americans and other minority groups. Note that although minority students account for 14.7 percent of the enrolled students in nursing, minority students account for only 10.9 percent of the degrees awarded in the past five years.

Recruitment

Part II of the questionnaire dealt with recruitment and showed that 93.5 percent of the responders had methods and/or strategies for recruiting minority students. The mean score of the 25 responders who rated the importance of these strategies on a score of 1-10 was 8.2 with a standard deviation of 1.5.

The methods and/or strategies identified by responders for recruiting minorities were categorized in seven general areas. The most frequently mentioned category was coordinate with campus-wide programs for minority recruitment, the next most frequent category was resources. Other categories were career fairs, work with feeder institutions, work with minority professional organizations, targeted contacts and other strategies. Table II lists detailed responses by category. The mean score of 6.3 with a standard deviation of 2 reflected how effective on a scale of 1-10 the 24 responders rated these strategies and/or methods. If they were not effective, the reasons for the lack of effectiveness were identified as too few applicants because there are not enough minorities in the state, admission requirements from the program are high, the applicant pool for the graduate level is limited, or nursing is not considered to be an attractive career. Limited resources were also identified as lack of consistent staffing, lack of resources to help students and high tuition. If they were effective, the most often cited reasons were on-campus visits, recruiting by current students and faculty and visits to high schools/feeder institutions. Most often cited barriers that prevent actively recruiting minorities were limited to funding, inability of minority students to meet admission requirements and lack of personal support services. Six responders indicated there are no barriers.

Retention

Part III of the questionnaire dealt specifically with retention. The barriers in retaining minority students in programs from the most difficult to the least difficult were identified. The top two barriers identified were inadequate student finance and inadequate basic skills. Six responders indicated that retention is not a problem, four indicated that there were not enough minorities here—student or faculty—three indicated that students work full or part-time and one identified lack of support services/mentors.

Institutions responded that the most effective strategy/method of retaining minority students was mentoring by peer students, upper division students, alumni, emeritus faculty, etc. Seven responders noted special attention to minority student needs: early warning, faculty counseling; six responders identified supportive services: tutorials, counseling, financial aid, writing center, etc.; five responders identified student groups and four stated financial aid/scholarships.

Table III provides the percent of yes responses to the question, "Are the strategies different for the level of students?." The table reflects that a number of responders do believe the retention strategies to be different for the level of students. Graduate recruitment was viewed as being different from undergraduate recruiting in the following ways: 1) Who is recruited and from where? Graduate recruiting is broader based, more sophisticated, relies more on personal contact and more out of state; 2) the provision of more supportive for undergraduates while faculty involvement is greater for graduate students; and 3) the difference in funding for undergraduate and graduate students.

Activities

In responding to the question that requested the responders to rank in order, activities that are used to enhance recruitment, enrollment, retention and graduation of minority students from the most important to the least important, seven responders referred to previous answers. On graduation, one responder identified the NCLEX review. On retention, the responses clustered around previous responses with mentoring, student services, peer groups and financial assistance dominating the list.

All 32 responders answered yes to the question, "Do you have minority faculty?." Thirty responders answered the question, "If so, how many?. The mean number of minority faculty in these institutions is 4.9 with a standard deviation of 3.2. In response to the request to rank in order activities that are used to assist majority faculty in enhancing the success of minority students in retention, recruitment and graduation from the most effective to the least effective, the most effective (N=10) were forums, workshops, seminars and programs on cultural diversity. Four responders noted helping faculty know where resources are available for minority students. The least effective method identified by only one person, covered a wide range of activities. Among them were, encourage majority faculty to become mentors for minority students and collaborate with other faculty at nearby universities on issues of diversity.

The two activities that ranked highest among 17 responders regarding activities of minority faculty that may enhance the potential success with minority students in recruitment, enrollment, retention, and graduation, the two that were ranked highest among 17 responders were mentoring/ role model and involve minority faculty with mentoring minority students. Opportunity was provided for responders to share comment about the recruitment, enrollment, retention and graduation of minority students.

Discussion

Recruitment was done by most of the responders and specific methods and/or strategies were used to recruit minority students. Specific strategies identified most for recruitment were coordinated with campus-wide program for minority recruitment, financial resources, career fairs, work with feeder institutions, and targeted contacts.

From inspection of the enrollment data, some of the institutions apparently marketed their undergraduate programs successfully based on the number of undergraduates that enrolled. The enrollment data, however, shows that proportionately the number of minority students to majority students enrolled in the three levels—undergraduate, masters and doctoral level programs and other specialty programs—is small. It should be noted that some responders indicated that nursing is not considered an attractive career. This reflects the importance of effective marketing of nursing. Without recruiters who can market the nursing profession well, the numbers attracted to it are likely to decline since there are numerous other opportunities available to students.

The relative frequency of enrollment is highest at the undergraduate baccalaureate level and then at the doctoral level with the lowest being at the master's level. Though more are enrolled in doctoral programs than masters, the numbers are still small. It should also be noted that though minority students may enroll in programs, those that are awarded degrees are considerably lower. Fewer Native Americans are enrolled than Asians and African Americans and fewer Hispanics are enrolled than African Americans.

The number of degrees awarded to minorities in the last five years is proportionately much lower than those awarded to majority students. Fewer Native Americans than African Americans, Hispanics or Asians are graduating. Though few, the numbers of African Americans, Asians and Hispanics are about the same proportionately. Attrition appears to be high in undergraduate programs considering the number that are admitted and the number graduated. Though the number completing baccalaureate degrees is small, it seems large enough that it would result in more minorities seeking graduate degrees. Since fewer are being retained and completing graduate degrees, the leadership pool of minority nurses is not likely to increase by much unless there are changes in the recruitment, enrollment and retention of minority students. It is not entirely clear whether there is a lag between recruitment efforts, retention and degree production.

Barriers identified most in the retention of minority students in nursing programs, were inadequate student finance and inadequate basic skills.

These responses raise the question as to whether some minorities have difficulty remaining in programs without help. It is not clear what "inadequate basic skills means. More information is needed to specifically address this concern. Six responders noted that retention was not a problem. However, these responders and others identified strategies that they found helpful to students. They were providing mentors, student services, peer group support, and financial assistance.

It is interesting to note that with so much discussion about diversity and multicultural populations in the 1990s, that responders did not identify strategies that specified cultural dimensions directly. None identified marketing as an important aspect of recruitment. The recognition of the need for nurse leaders among minorities did not emerge as a concern in the recruitment, retention or graduation of students in nursing.

Implications

The inclusion of minority students in nursing is not about fairness. It is a practical matter in terms of helping to provide health care to those who need it regardless of their ethnic group. A group of UCSF researchers, including Miriam Komaromy, Kevin Grumbach, Michael Drake and Andrew Bindman found that ethnicity, even more than poverty, is the greatest predictor of the adequacy of a community's medical services (Tevis 1995). Though their research was about physicians, similar arguments could be given for nurses considering that the researchers found that minority communities experienced the highest number of preventable hospitalizations—serious conditions that could have been avoided through appropriate primary care.

By the year 2000, the United States will have a non-white population of 67 million people. At the turn of the century, one in every four Americans will be Black, Hispanic, Middle Easterner or Asian (Cetron 1989). The number of minorities being cared for in the health care system is a practical reason to find means to recruit, minorities to enter nursing and to use strategies that will assure retention and graduation of those capable of practicing.

While this investigation provided worthwhile information, the sample was drawn from major research institutions and not from all types of institutions of higher learning that offer baccalaureate and graduate degrees in nursing. This limitation suggests that a more widely representative sample should be considered if this study is replicated. Though a stratified sample was used, no power analyses were done to determine the probability of making type II errors when conducting the tests of significance. The responses on Part IV of the questionnaire may need to be revised as some respondents felt they had already answered the questions and provided little or no additional information. One question that should have been asked was how many total faculty did the nursing school/college have. This would have helped put in perspective the average number (4.9) of minority faculty. It is not known whether 4.9 is a reasonable proportion of the faculty or a small proportion of the faculty for this specific sample. I have concluded that it is small based on the National League for Nursing 1990 data source which showed that 91.2 percent of the faculty who were teaching nursing were White; 5.8 percent Black; 2.56 percent Asian; 1.6 percent Hispanic and less than 1 percent Native American (NLN 1990).

One limitation was who completed the questionnaire that was sent to the Dean. Some responders provided detailed definitive information while some responders were less detailed, and in some instances minimal information was provided. If a means can be used to, at least, determine the title or position of the person completing the questionnaire, this may help in analyzing the data and account for the type of response received.

The data obtained from this study reflects that there are formal commitments to diversity in the institutions, particularly in the area of recruiting minority students into nursing. Only two institutions reported having no strategies or methods for recruiting minority students. Finding means to provide financial assistance to students seems to be an important dimension in retention in the programs. This was the most often noted barrier in retaining minority students. The second most noted was inadequate basic skills. Exactly what the responders meant by inadequate skills is not entirely clear. In ranking the method that is most effective in retaining minority students, mentoring was the response most often identified.

Careers in academic nursing do not appear to be generally encouraged. Except for the ethnic minority program directed by the American Nurses Association, there is no other program with a highly visible reputation for encouraging nurses to consider academic careers. After three decades of the enactment of equal opportunity legislation, minorities make up only a tiny percent of the faculties in many of the institutions of higher education in America.

The Pew Health Professions Commission noted that "a substantial body of literature concludes that culturally sensitive care is good care. This means two things for all health professional schools. First, they must continue their commitment to ensuring that the students they train represent the rich ethnic diversity of our society. . . Second, diversifying the entering class is not sufficient to ensure understanding and appreciation of diversity. Cultural sensitivity must be a part of the educational experience that touches the life of every student (Pew Health Professions Commission 1995).

The changes in the health care system suggest that professional nurses will need to be prepared to deliver care in a variety of settings in the community. Nurses, including minority nurses, who are prepared at the baccalaureate, masters and doctoral level as leaders can help develop new models of integration between education and the managed care systems. More research that includes diverse populations will be needed to assist policy-makers in formulating more effective health care delivery policies.

Psychologically in the United States, persons of color are still marginalized and face discrimination regardless of their success. However, it seems reasonable to assume that the institutions of higher education are in a unique position to help Americans make diversity work in this society. The American Commitments National Panel believes it is possible to create inclusive learning environments (AACU 1995, 40). Higher education can support forms of public learning with integrity if our campuses are inclusive and engaged in learning and producing knowledge through diverse perspectives and diverse people. Creating environments where students from every background have a full experience of equity maybe awhile coming. However, it is essential that strategies that aid in enhancing the recruitment, enrollment, retention and graduation of minorities in nursing, be identified and used. The health care needs of the growing minority population must be met. Minority nurses should be involved in meeting this need and contributing to the integrated system of health care delivery that is evolving in the nation.

Summary

This survey, based on the response from thirty-two institutions, identified a number of issues related to the recruitment, retention and graduation of minorities in nursing. Different strategies for recruitment were mentioned for undergraduates and graduate minority students. Undergraduate recruitment tends to rely on feeder schools, is limited primarily to the geographic catchment area of the institution and encompasses broader efforts to attract minorities. Graduate level recruitment is from a larger geographical area and relies more on personal contacts. The more selective institutions identified the lack of a large pool of qualified minority applicants as a barrier to recruitment, and almost all institutions identified a lack of adequate financial resources as a significant barrier. Successful retention of minority students requires strong personal support services ranging from advising to mentoring. The need for additional staff also seemed important in providing the required personal support services. The survey revealed a gap between the level of minority enrollment (14.7 percent of nursing students) and minority graduates (10.9 percent of nursing degrees). It is not clear whether this gap is due to a simple time lag for recent recruits to pass through the institution or due to barriers such as academic difficulties. Financial aid was the most frequently mentioned barrier to completion of a degree program.

References

Association of American Colleges and Universities (AACU). 1995. *The drama of diversity and democracy. Higher education and American commitments*. Washington, DC: Association of American Colleges and Universities.

Cetron, M., and D. Davis 1989. *American renaissance*. New York: St. Martin's Press.

Lewin, M, and B. Rice, eds. 1994. *Balancing the scales of opportunity in health care: Ensuring racial and ethnic diversity in the health professions*. Washington, DC: National Academy Press.

National League for Nursing (NLN). 1990. *National League for Nursing Data Source*. New York: National League for Nursing.

Pew Health Profession Commission. 1995. *Critical Challenges: Revitalizing the Health Professions for the Twenty First Century. The Third Report of the Pew Health Professions Commission*.

Tevis, Y.P., ed. 1995. UCSF undeferred from goal of diversity. *USSF Mosaic Diversity at the University of California* 2(1): 3.

4   The Qualification Dilemma

Dalmas A. Taylor, PhD

Brown v. Board of Education of Topeka (1954) struck a near fatal blow to 300 years of color separation. The decree affirmed that separate facilities for Blacks and Whites were inherently unequal. Although *Brown* addressed separation in educational facilities, the decision had implications for public and private accommodations. Yet an unacceptable amount of racial apartheid remains a fact of life in the United States. Centuries of cultural and institutional racism have resulted in a codification of practices that defy change. Psychometric practice in education and industry have aided and abetted an accommodation of the status quo.

Test scores have been used to determine who qualifies for entrance or participation in a variety of institutional settings, not least among them employment and education. In some instances the validity of the tests was never considered. This practice has resulted in a multimillion dollar testing industry. Conservative estimates of these costs used by the testing industry itself exceed $100 million per year! In the years 1992–93 alone at least 14.5 million students in K–12 took some form of standardized test. Additional testing outside the education arena contributes to the magnitude of this industry.

In this chapter, the efficacy of this practice, especially as it pertains to women and people of color, will be challenged. An alternative approach to selection and admission that will be more inclusive and equitable than current approaches will be proposed. This challenge will highlight the dilemma inherent in the way we define qualification.

The Testing Controversy

The first testing was probably done by the Chinese as a way of selecting applicants for their civil service. These tests were based on skills specifically needed in the job (good handwriting, knowledge of government, etc.) as opposed to general cognitive ability. More recently, in the 19th century, the French government commissioned Alfred Binet to test young children to identify those whose lack of success in normal classrooms could be addressed by some form of special education. Binet's work led to the development of what has become widely known as the IQ test (Binet 1909). Binet's test was modified by Stanford University psychologist Lewis Terman—thus the name Stanford-Binet. This approach launched the testing industry in its quest to measure mental abilities. Having established a methodology to determine mental capacity, it was a short leap to move to employing the new found methodology to the prediction and determination of standards for job placement, admission to colleges and universities, and other applications.

Binet feared the abuse of his instrument. He predicted that the score would be used as an indelible label rather than as a guide for identifying children who needed help. Binet believed IQ was only a rough empirical guide useful for a limited applied purpose and was not an entity unto itself, such as height. He not only refused to label IQ as inborn intelligence but also declined to see it as a device for ranking children according to mental worth. Further, he feared that the IQ label would act as a self-fulfilling prophesy thereby diverting a child's behavior into a predicted path. The proper use of the test, he declared, was to identify children whose poor performance indicated a need for special education. American psychologists perverted Binet's intention and advanced the concept of hereditarian IQ by assuming that intelligence was largely inherited. The ensuing controversy between hereditarians and their opponents, who viewed intelligence principally as a learned measure which could be improved with training, continues to this day (e.g., Herrnstein and Murray 1994).

A common finding in the literature that documents Black-White IQ differences is central to the debate between the hereditarians and the environmentalists. The heritability studies are largely correlational, in that they involve two factors that can change at the same time in the same or different directions without being affected by the other. On the other hand, experimental techniques lead to inferences of causality, and when these approaches are used differences in exam scores between racial groups disappear (Aronson and Bridgeman 1979). Additionally, the incontrovertible genetic evidence supports the conclusion that human beings belong to one indivisible species. We have yet to find evidence pointing to DNA, genes or chromosomes as a basis for explaining differences in White and Black IQ scores.

Not surprisingly, IQ and other tests employed to determine qualification have been criticized as being culturally biased and thereby causing an unfair exclusion of Blacks and other ethnic minorities. As Dawes, for example, (1993) pointed out: "Aptitude tests can't be neutral to experience because aptitude itself isn't neutral to experience" (p. 33). The behaviors we presume to measure by any test are embedded in experience, and experience is affected by customs and traditions as defined and practiced by a given society. In the case of the United States these customs and traditions have been heavily influenced by racial and gender discrimination. It follows that the application of test scores for selection and admissions purposes has largely resulted in outcomes that closely reflect the unfair practices of society.

Experimental Approach to Measurement

Psychology's stance on measurement is well articulated by Stevens (1951) in the *Handbook of Experimental Psychology*. "The stature of a science is commonly measured by the degree to which it makes use of mathematics" (p. 1). Yet, as Stevens goes on to say, mathematics itself is not a science, but a formal and logical symbolic system—a game of signs and rules. More important, he concludes "at no place is there perfect correspondence between the mathematical model and the empirical variables of the material universe" (p. 1). The significance of this latter observation should never escape us and indeed should fuel our caution and humility as we employ measurement in the determination of applicant qualifications. Measurement is simply the assignment of numbers to objects and events according to agreed upon rules. These considerations are addressed later in this chapter.

Racial Norming

Test administrators have used score adjustment to compensate for disparity in test scores between ethnic and gender groups. Approaches involve converting scores to percentiles within race or gender groups, adding a fixed number of points to the scores of particular groups, and so on. As Sackett and Wilk (1994) pointed out, disputes about score adjustment can be argued on legal, technical and social grounds. Legally, before the Civil Rights Act of 1991, various commentators differed strongly as to the permissibility of the practice (e.g., Delahunty 1988; Hartigan and Wigdor 1989). On technical grounds, score adjustment may be offered as a mechanism to eliminate bias measurement. On social grounds, arguments tend to be cast in terms of individual merit (micro justice) versus general societal (macro justice) good. Opponents of score adjustment tend to argue for the sanctity of individual merit and the inappropriateness of minority group membership as a factor in selection decisions (e.g., Gottfredson 1988). Arguments regarding attaching social stigma to members of the aided minority group are also common (Sackett and Wilk 1994, 931). Sackett and Wilk (1994) organized these arguments into three categories: (1) *philosophical*, minority preference as a value to achieve increased minority representation; (2) *measurement bias*, when a given test score does not carry the same meaning for members in all groups, score adjustment is needed; and (3) *fair test use*, score adjustment is warranted when a particular way of using a test is at odds with an espoused position of what constitutes fair test use (Sackett and Wilk 1994, 931).

In the early 1980s the United States Employment Service (USES) began the practice of converting test scores to percentile scores within racial and ethnic groups to compensate for test score disparity among racial groups. The adjusted scores were used to refer candidates to prospective employers on the basis of within-group percentile scores. Thus the same raw score was converted to a different percentile score depending on the race of the examinee. The practice, however, was challenged by the U.S. Department of Justice as unfair. The Civil Rights Act of 1991 protested this practice, thereby making racial norming and similar approaches illegal.

Performance As Selection Criterion

Black-White differences in ratings of job performance tend to be small, whereas differences in Black-White performance on standardized tests are large. Thus, if job performance is used as a selection criterion, differences in the representations of Blacks and Whites in the job force would be small. If job selection or college admission is based on tests, as they usually are, then there would be large differences in the selected population in favor of Whites. Thus, de facto, tests are a means of securing preferential selection for Whites. Without tests, many Whites who perform more poorly on the job than do Blacks would not be hired. There are essentially two reasons for test bias that have been consistently reported in the literature: (1) cultural bias (e.g., Dawes 1993; Klineberg 1935) and (2) the inability of tests to predict completely all aspects of a given job (Sackett and Wilk 1994). Bias in testing calls into question fairness in selection procedures in which tests are employed.

Some years ago, Thorndike (1971) proposed a model to deal with selection system fairness, in which the success rate is determined for each group in an applicant population. Success is defined as the proportion of job applicants who would exceed a specified level of performance if hired. For a selection system to be fair, he argued, the rate of selection from each group must be proportional to these success rates. Only when majority-minority differences on selection devices are equal in magnitude to majority-minority differences in job performance can the selection system be deemed fair. A variety of other fairness models were developed about the same time as Thorndike's approach (for a review of these models see Hunter and Schmidt 1976; Peterson and Novick 1976; Schmidt and Hunter 1974).

The admissions process has transformed university and other institutional personnel into gatekeepers of opportunity and privilege. For the social psychologist this is an issue of allocation or distributive justice. In discussing distributive justice, Deutsch (1975) delineated conditions that give rise to three justice principles: equity, equality and need. According to Deutsch, equity predominates when economic productivity is the primary goal. Equality is advanced when the common goal is to maintain positive social relations. And, finally, the principle of need prevails when the goal is to advance personal development and welfare. These distinctions, however, challenge and may be offensive to traditional notions of meritocracy in which fairness is conceived as outcomes that are proportional to individual abilities, the quality of their input, or both. The conflict here is one of micro- and macro-justice—individual merit versus group justice. Affirmative action remedies were designed to address the latter.

Gender and Ethnic Inequities

The United States has not reached her ideal of achieving equity for all of its citizens. Census data, for example, reveal the following: 1989 per family member median income for Black families was $4,832, whereas for White families it was $9,421 (U.S. Bureau of the Census 1991, 38, Table 43). In that same year salaries for White women in the labor force were a mere 66.5 percent of White men's salaries. Further, Black and non-White women earned less than men (U.S. Bureau of the Census 1991, 457, Table 736). A large number of studies indicate that differences in income and wealth are attributable to ethnic and gender discrimination (Bergmann 1986; Crosby 1991; Faludi 1991; Rhode 1989). It is also likely the case that test measurement played some role in creating the situations that led to these differences.

Title VII of the 1964 Civil Rights Act was intended to address the inequalities in American culture that created and sustained the racial and gender disparities described in the statistics cited earlier. The challenges to the remedies that emanated from Title VII initiatives were as aggressive, if not more so, than the remedies themselves. Affirmative action, the most controversial of the measures designed to eliminate the vestiges of racial and gender discrimination, continues to be challenged to this day. Yet, as Hacker (1992) noted, "white America continues to ask of its Black citizens an extra patience and perseverance that whites have never required of themselves" (p. 219).

In the early 1990s, a White Georgetown law student named Timothy Maguire wrote an article titled "Admissions Apartheid" for a student publication, republished in Commentary (1992) as "My Bout with Affirmative Action," in which he charged that Black law students at Georgetown were not as qualified as White law students. Black students, he argued, had lower scores on the Law Schools Admissions Test (LSAT); additionally, he observed that they had low grade point averages. The ensuing public controversy stimulated by these assertions is less relevant here than the facts and declarations from law school officials during the debate. Fact One: Maguire's own LSAT scores were below the median for Georgetown students. Fact Two: Maguire was admitted to Georgetown through a special program for "low testers." He had been given extra points on his admission profile for having served in the Peace Corps in

Africa. Fact Three: Associate Dean Ted Miller acknowledged that the escalating number of applicants caused law schools to turn to the LSAT as an artificial means to help them screen applications. As the number of applications increased, the minimum LSAT score (the qualified threshold) rose. However, many who achieved the previously lower scores turned out to be distinguished lawyers. Miller, speaking for the school, not only revealed the arbitrary nature of determining qualification but also gave evidence that determining what it means to be qualified is not as easy as it is often made to seem. A recent challenge to admissions practices at The University of Texas Law School gives further evidence of the qualification problem. A White applicant sued the law school when she was turned down despite having a higher grade point average and test scores than those of a majority of the Blacks and Latinos who were accepted. In a surprising outcome, the federal district court ruled in favor of the plaintiff but defended the law school as having a legally sufficient reason to justify racial practices.

Law schools are not alone in facing the dilemmas associated with standardized test scores and admission practices in the context of affirmative action. In 1978 the Supreme Court ruled in a 5–4 decision that the medical school at the University of California-Davis unlawfully discriminated against Allan Bakke by rejecting his application while at the same time setting aside 16 of its 100 places for minority students, at least some of whom had test scores lower than Bakke's scores (*Regents of the University of California v. Bakke* 1978). The court also ruled, in the same case, that race could be considered as one factor in the admissions decision. More recently, University of California medical schools have once again been accused of unfairly and unlawfully favoring minorities in admissions. The evidence cited was presented in the form of a scattergram representing each applicant admitted by the University of California at San Diego between 1987 and 1993, with the undergraduate grade point average on one axis and the standardized medical school aptitude test score on the other. Majority students were virtually all clustered in the upper right quadrant of the graph, representing high grade point averages and high test scores, whereas the targeted minorities were clustered in the lower left quadrant, representing the lowest grades and scores. The regents were divided in their support of the medical school's admissions practices.

Affirmative Action

Dawes (1993) attempted to resolve the problem of unfairness in test situations that gave advantage to one group over another as a function of cultural experience. Dawes's remedy, called "racial norming," involves interpreting a given raw score on a test relative to the average on the test of the applicant's membership group, rather than relative to the overall average of all applicants. The advantage offered by this approach is that qualifications are not ignored. A well-qualified majority will be admitted, and a poorly-qualified ethnic minority would still be denied admission. The downside of this approach, as Dawes sees it, is for the ambiguous cases that fall near the cutoff score. And because it is these cases for which the predictive powers of our tests are least reliable, any damage is minimal compared to the fairness achieved for both groups, he concludes.

Dawes's application of racial norming represents an attempt to address the perceived contradiction of the "color blind" and "color sensitive" issues witnessed in the 1978 Bakke Supreme Court case. This approach fuels the perception that affirmative action focuses on group membership to the exclusion of merit.

The policy of affirmative action was promulgated largely to encourage aggressive means to overcome the negative effects of present and past discrimination in employment and admissions practices. Because precise measures of implementation were not spelled out, there have been numerous applications and an equal number of objections from doubters. As Turner and Pratkanis (1994) pointed out, plans may focus on recruitment, selection, or promotion; and implementation may include specialized training, altering the use of selection criteria, broadening the scope of recruitment activities, or any number of other approaches to remedying deficiency in the utilization of targeted groups. Turner and Pratkanis went on to say that one of the most controversial aspects of affirmative action concerns the qualification issue.

Opponents of affirmative action assert that preferential treatment and other "artificial" remedies in affirmative action procedures result in the selection of unqualified individuals. However, as we know, exclusive use of these qualifications in admissions and selection decisions is much less frequent than most believe to be the case. Often decisions in this arena turn on issues such as nepotism, a relationship with an important benefactor, and the like. The empirical research on affirmative action provides little guidance on its effects on the measurement of qualification in the selection process (Crosby 1994; Nacoste 1994; Taylor 1994; Turner and Pratkanis 1994). However, some researchers have discussed how the perception of preferential treatment can be motivated by racism. Murrell and her colleagues (Murrell, Dietz-Uhler, Dovidio, Gaertner, and Drout 1994) demonstrated more White resistance to affirmative action for Blacks compared to affirmative action for others, such as the handicapped or the elderly. Despite Jackie Robinson's phenomenal talents in college sports, when he was integrated into major league baseball many Whites viewed him as preferentially selected for the Brooklyn Dodgers because of his race (Pratkanis and Turner 1994a, 1994b). Racism leads to perceptions of preferential selection.

Most authors agree that both positive outcomes and, in some instances, negative consequences are found when the issue of qualification is examined in the context of affirmative action procedures. These studies, like many in our discipline, tease out complexities in what otherwise seems a fairly simple and straightforward process—establishing standards and criteria in selecting qualified applicants. Georgetown Associate

Dean Miller, without the benefit of sophisticated statistics, seemed to understand this better than most of us. Distinguished lawyers, most or all of whom were probably White men, would not have been allowed to practice law had they applied to Georgetown 2 or 3 years subsequent to the date of their original application, at which time the cutoff scores on the LSAT had been raised in response to increasing enrollment pressures. The dilemma then is this: As long as individuals are capable of doing the work, who is to say they are unqualified?

American psychologists misused Binet's principles and consequently perverted scientific applications of testing to human behavior. Two fallacies account for this abuse: reification and hereditarianism. Reification assumes that test scores represent a single scaleable thing in the head of the person being tested. Hereditarianism, on the other hand, implies a genetic basis for scores within groups that is generalizable to behaviors between groups. In both instances the concepts were enforced by individuals who used the tests to maintain social ranks and distinctions in human populations. The ultimate dream here was the creation of a rational society in which professions would be allocated by mental measurement. Even a casual analysis of our history reveals that these aspirations have been more an illusion of meritocracy and fairness than the reality of their applications.

Interestingly, some of the attacks on quality and diversity come from Black conservatives whose arguments carry weight as "authenticators" of the minority experience. To name a few examples: Carter's (1991) *Reflections of an Affirmative Action Baby*, Sowell's (1984) *Civil Rights: Rhetoric or Reality?* or Steele's (1990) *The Content of our Character.* Other attacks can be found in Glazer's (1976) *Affirmative Discrimination*, Schlesinger's (1992) *The Disuniting of America*, and Hirsch's (1987) *Cultural Literacy.* Common to these works is the underlying premise that meritocracy is simply the equating of merit with just rewards. Therefore, unjust rewards come from lack of merit. Dawes (1993) conceded that his "racial norming" approach involves unfairness because there is no way to treat everyone fairly at once. Remember Dawes's concern that tie scores or scores within the test's margin of error are acceptable, but a six-point difference is not. Hence, a single point is critical, whereas we ignore five. Is this an issue of psychometric precision or psychometric arrogance?

Future Directions

Ezorsky (1991) proposed a method of selection that is useful in our thinking about future directions in employing tests to determine qualification. For Ezorsky, qualification should be based on candidates meeting at least the minimum qualifications for the job available. Members of underrepresented groups who are in that set may be selected over other people in the set. This approach is similar to the concept of *banding* in which all scores within a certain standard deviation are treated the same. This makes use of the statistical notion of significance—two scores are the same unless they are statistically different. The difficulty here is similar to that experienced by Dawes. Where should the cutoff points be drawn? Although the scores within a band are not statistically different, the scores just above and just below the cutoff are not statistically different from adjacent scores within the band. What is attractive about this approach is that it does not presume that distinctions can be made between members of a qualified set so long as they all can do the job. The willingness to identify underrepresented individuals in this approach is to acknowledge cultural handicaps that tell us little or nothing about one's ability to perform, but may tell us a great deal about contaminations in determining who is qualified.

In his 1993 address to the American Psychological Association, "Racism and Civil Rights: Right Problem, Wrong Solution," Jones (1993) alerted us to the dangers of viewing individualism as a criterion of cultural success. There are built-in biases favoring some individuals because of their accumulated group experience, and disadvantages for other individuals because of their group-based status. He concluded the point by asking the question, which was probably rhetorical, "Once a minimum competence threshold is reached, what are the relevant criteria that should determine success?" The concepts of "qualified sets" and "minimum competence thresholds" have relevance here.

Steven (1951) defined threshold as "the value that divides the continuum into two classes (or sets). . . . Thus, the threshold may be regarded as a 'cut' in the continuum of stimuli. . .neither of which has a terminus in the region of the cut" (p. 33). In describing absolute and differential thresholds Steven offered these techniques as procedures for sampling and interpolating behaviors on a continuum—analogous to what mathematicians do when they trap the values of an irrational number narrowing the gap between two rational numbers, one larger and one smaller than the irrational in question. In psychophysics what gets recorded as the threshold is an arbitrary point within a range of variability, somewhere in the gap between stimuli that are definitely above threshold and stimuli definitely below threshold.

It is my contention that the demarcation between a qualified population and an unqualified population is a problem of psychophysics—one in which the concept of threshold has much to offer. Yet, we continue to rely on absolute cuts in test scores in making admissions and selection decisions. As long as this is the case, we will witness lawsuits reminiscent of the 1987 Bakke case in which the University of California—Davis was successfully challenged in its affirmative action admission policy for medical students. As a matter of fact, the four White students who filed a lawsuit against the University of Texas in Austin claimed that they were denied admission to the law school while at the same time students of color with both lower grade point averages and LSAT scores were admitted. Court documents of records between 1984 and 1991 confirm lower grade point averages and LSAT scores for Blacks and Hispanics.

In 1992 the average grade point and LSAT scores for Whites were 3.52 and 162, respectively. The relevant data the same year for people of color were 3.31 and 158, respectively. Lawyers for the university assert that all students admitted were qualified and ranked in the 75th to 85th percentile on the LSAT. These scores probably did not differ statistically from each other.

If the law school acknowledged that the percentile score can arbitrarily be used to define two populations—one qualified for admission and one not—it would be on much safer ground in defending its admissions practices. To do so, however, would also require it to acknowledge that differences on any measure or attribute between candidates above this threshold are irrelevant to the criteria of qualification. Such a position would render meaningless the argument that individuals with higher test scores are more qualified than individuals with lower test scores.

This thesis lacks a well-developed quantified path to its conclusion, but does lay out a conceptual argument consistent with our knowledge of psychophysical applications to human behavior. Once again we are challenged to employ this knowledge in ameliorating the racial chasm in the United States. In *The Dallas Morning News*, columnist Clarence Page (1994) recently declared that "America's racial past unavoidably haunts its present and nags at its future" (p. 13A). The point of his essay was the futility of Black Americans' expectation of any form of reparations for the evils of slavery. However, he was sanguine that provisions for public education and job opportunities would in the long run be as valuable, if not more so. As gatekeepers we have an opportunity to make it possible for others, especially those disadvantaged by past and present discrimination, to have opportunities.

It has been said that we live at a level of abstraction that obscures our ability to discern fundamental meaning and values. And through our legal system we have the ability to assign value and ownership to absolutely everything. This is precisely what we have done with education, for instance. We need to remember that in preliterate society human knowledge belonged to everyone, and everyone was equally entitled and had a right to accumulated human knowledge.

We have made education a property and through our credentials and arbitrary conventions we have decided who shall and shall not own property. And so it is with jobs and a number of other commodities that we have a right to access. Every individual has the right to his or her mind and body and may come to any institutional setting to develop his or her productive capacity, contribute to human knowledge, and otherwise benefit from society's largess. Those of us who are degreed or otherwise privileged are only custodians, trustees if you will, who hold knowledge in trust for humanity, and are obliged to pursue equitable arrangements in the allocation of resources and commodities.

The increasing diversity in our culture and its implications for the nursing workforce of the future make it imperative that we promote standards that are inclusive and predictive of ability to perform. The nursing profession has the capacity to do this and to do so within the boundaries of their mission to promote human welfare. Some have argued that affirmative action is justified as a form of reparation for the evils of the past, whereas others argue that it leads to stigmatization. The remedy proposed here avoids both contentions. It argues simply that the determination of qualification is a psychophysical matter that can be resolved by establishing the threshold between two populations: the qualified (those who can perform) and the unqualified (those who cannot perform). Selection within the former population can, in theory, be accomplished by using noncognitive variables in assigning weights consistent with desired societal outcomes, or assigning weights to variables that might be more predictive of job success than are scores on a test (e.g., relevant experience and interpersonal or communication skills).

References

Aronson, E., and D. Bridgeman. 1979. Jigsaw groups and the desegregated class roll: In pursuit of common goals. *Personality and Social Psychology Bulletin* 5: 438–446.

Bergmann, B.R. 1986. *The economic emergence of women*. New York: Basic Books.

Binet, A. 1909. *Les idées modernes sur les enfants* [Modern ideas about children]. Paris: Flammarion.

Brown v. Board of Educ., 347 U.S. 483 (1954).

Carter, S.L. 1992. *Reflections of an affirmative action baby*. New York: Basic Books.

Civil Rights Act of 1964, Pub. L. No. 88–352, §78 Stat. 243 (1964).

Civil Rights Act of 1991, Pub. L. No. 102–166, §105 Stat. 1071 (Nov. 21, 1991).

Crosby, F.J. 1991. *Juggling: The unexpected advantages of balancing career and home for women and their families*. New York: Free Press.

Crosby, F.J. 1994. Understanding affirmative action. *Basic and Applied Social Psychology* 15: 13–41.

Dawes, R.M. 1993. Aptitude tests can't be neutral to experience because aptitude itself isn't neutral to experience. *Academe* 79: 31–34.

Delahunty, R J. 1988. Perspectives on within group scoring. *Journal of Vocational Behavior* 33: 463–477.

Deutsch, M. 1975. Equality, equity, and need: What determines which value will be used as a basis of distributive justice? *Journal of Social Issues* 31: 137–149.

Ezorsky, G. 1991. *Racism and justice: The case for affirmative action*. Ithaca, NY: Cornell University Press.

Faludi, S. 1991. *Backlash: The undeclared war against American women*. New York: Crown.

Glazer, N. 1976. *Affirmative discrimination: Ethnic inequality and public policy*. Cambridge, MA: Harvard University Press

Gottfredson, L. 1988. Reconsidering fairness: A matter of social and ethical priorities. *Journal of Vocational Behavior* 33: 293–319.

Hacker, A. 1992. *Two nationals: Black and white, separate, hostile, unequal.* New York: Scribner's.

Hartigan, S.A., and A.K. Wigdor, eds. 1989. *Fairness in employment testing: Validity generalization minority issues and general aptitude test battery.* Washington, DC: National Academy Press.

Herrnstein, R.J., and C. Murray. 1994. *The bell curve: Intelligence and class structure in American Life.* New York: Free Press.

Hirsch, E.D. 1987. *Cultural literacy: What every American needs to know.* Boston: Houghton Mifflin.

Hunter, J.E., and F.L. Schmidt. 1976. Critical analysis of the statistical and ethical implications of various definitions of test bias. *Psychological Bulletin* 83: 1053–1071.

Jones, J.M. 1993. Racism and civil rights: Right problem, wrong solution. Paper presented at the meeting of the American Psychological Association, Toronto, Canada. August.

Klineberg, O. 1935. *Race differences.* New York: Harper & Row.

Maguire, T. 1992. My bout with affirmative action. *Commentary* 2a: 50–52.

Murrell, A.J., B.L. Dietz-Uhler, J.F. Dovidio, S.L. Gaertner, and C. Drout. 1994. *Basic and Applied Social Psychology* 15: 71–84.

Nacoste, R.B. 1994. If empowerment is the goal . . . Affirmative action and social interaction. *Basic and Applied Social Psychology* 15: 87–112.

Page, C. 1994. America can pay its debt to blacks with jobs, schooling. The Dallas Morning News, August 2, 13A.

Peterson, N.S., and M.R. Novick. 1976. An evaluation of some models for culture fair selection. *Journal of Educational Measurement* 13: 3–29.

Pratkanis, A.R., and M.E. Turner. 1994a. Nine principles of successful affirmative action.: Mr. Branch Rickey, Mr. Jackie Robinson, and the integration of baseball. *NINE: A Journal of Baseball History and Social Policy Perspectives* 3: 36–65.

Pratkanis, A.R., and M.E. Turner. 1994b. The year cool Papa Bell lost the batting title: Mr. Branch Rickey and Mr. Jackie Robinson's plea for affirmative action. *NINE: A Journal of Baseball History and Social Policy Perspectives* 2: 260–276.

Regents of the University of California v. Bakke, 438 U.S. 265 (1978).

Rhode, D.L. 1989. *Justice and gender: Sex discrimination and the law.* Cambridge, MA: Harvard University Press.

Sackett, P.R., and S.L. Wilk. 1994. Within group norming and other forms of score adjustment in preemployment testing. *American Psychologist* 49: 929–954.

Schlesinger, A.M. 1992. *The disuniting of America.* New York: Norton.

Schmidt, F.L., and J.E. Hunter. 1974. Racial and ethnic bias in psychological tests: Divergent implications of two definitions of test bias. *American Psychologist* 29: 1–8.

Sowell, T. 1984. *Civil Rights: Rhetoric or reality?* New York: Morrow:

Steele, S. 1990. *The content of our character: A new vision of race in America.* New York: St. Martin's Press.

Steven, S.S. 1951. *Handbook of experimental psychology.* New York: Wiley.

Taylor, M.C. 1994. Impact of affirmative action on beneficiary groups: Evidence from the 1990 General Social Survey. *Basic and Applied Social Psychology* 15: 143–178.

Thorndike, R.L. 1971. Concepts of cultural fairness. *Journal of Educational Measurement* 8: 63–70.

Turner, M.E., and A.R. Pratkanis. 1994. A review of recipient reaction to preferential selection and affirmative action. *Basic and Applied Social Psychology* 15: 43–69.

U.S. Bureau of the Census. 1991. *Statistical abstract of the United States, 1991: The national data book.* Washington, DC: U.S. Department of Commerce.

51

The Qualification Dilemma

Part Two

Nursing
Issues
for
Populations
of
Color

5

Higher Education and the African American Experience: Barriers to Success and Remedies for Failure

Romeria Tidwell, PhD

Gordon Berry, EdD

Historical Perspectives

It will come as no surprise, even to the casual social observer, for us to state that higher education in the United States was historically designed to serve a special group of people. The net result of this social policy is that higher education has traditionally belonged to middle and upper class men and women. This class-driven model has been especially true for those institutions with a student population composed predominantly of White Americans. Indeed, American higher education fostered a culture of being the sanctuary for those select White Americans, especially men, for whom it was thought could most profit from the advance training.

Prior to the Civil War, for example, Black Americans were naturally excluded from higher education, as well as most formal common school educational opportunities. During the century after the Civil War, when African Americans succeeded in creating college opportunities for thousands of their youth, two principal obstacles prevented the fullest growth: (1) the positive disinclination of White-controlled institutions, North and South, to share their resources with minority youth; and (2) the unrelenting preoccupation of public policy, on all governmental levels, to restrict educational opportunities to the children of dominant social groups (Weinberg 1977; Tidwell and Berry 1993).

It took the *Brown v. Board of Education of Topeka* in 1954 to declare that segregation in public schools was unconstitutional. Relying heavily on social science research, the Supreme Court declared:

> that to separate Negro pupils from others of similar age and qualifications solely because of their race generates a feeling of inferiority as to their status in the community

that may affect their hearts and minds in a way unlikely
ever to be undone.

Significantly, we are still so impacted by the race issue in the United
States that we continue to find ourselves attempting to implement the
promise of Brown. It could be that after years of functioning in a social
system that mandated second class citizenship for minorities, ideas about
the inferiority and superiority of various groups are too deeply en-
trenched for society to manage change.

Pinkney (1975) suggests that the negative attitudes of Whites toward
Blacks and other people of color became part of the "American way of
life." As psychologists and other students of behavior can appreciate,
years of being perceived as a second class person and having it substanti-
ated in lesser employment, segregated education, and restrictions on
living areas can cause some African Americans and other people of color
to believe that their skin color, language, and general cultural beliefs are
not appreciated in American society. When these destructive influences
effect minority group members, it is possible to see the impact of these
negative messages cutting at the very core of their self-concept and
achievement motivation. Without some real psychological, economic,
social, and/or political impetus, the cumulative effects of a system designed to keep people of color out of the mainstream of American higher
education could and has worked to retard their progress.

Reginald Wilson (1994) argues that there were two revolutions in federal
initiatives, Supreme Court actions, and congressional laws that provided
the impetus to African American and other minority participation in
higher education. The first revolution in minority access to higher education occurred with the passage of the GI Bill for educational benefits in
1945. The second revolution took place with the 1964 Civil Rights Act
that was built on John F. Kennedy's Great Society programs such as the
Office of Economic Opportunity (Wilson 1994).

Although some African Americans were attending both public and private
colleges and universities throughout the country during the 1960s, the
large majority of these students were in what is now known as Historically
Black Colleges and Universities (HBCUs). These colleges, with founding
dates as early as 1854, began to grow after the Emancipation Proclamation
of 1863, and most were established in the South by northern religious
groups to educate the freed slaves. With the passage of the Morill McCo-
mas Act of 1890, the states were allowed to establish "separate but equal"
publicly supported land-grant colleges designed for Blacks. By 1938, 97
percent of all Black students in American higher education attended
these Black colleges, and nearly 65 percent of African Americans were
attending HBCUs in 1965. It is important to note that about 40 percent
of all African Americans in college were attending predominantly White
institutions in 1954, the year of the Brown decision. Before desegregation,
however, the HBCUs educated the overwhelming majority of African
American physicians, lawyers and teachers (Wilson 1994).

It was during the Civil Rights Movement of the 1960s that there were some attempts by a number of predominantly White institutions of higher education to increase the number of African American and other students of color enrolled on their campuses. Some of these programs supporting the admission of minorities were so busy looking for the model disadvantaged young person who had all of the exotic features of poverty and poor school performance, that some men and women from limited income families with good educational records were overlooked. There were also programs that, from the very beginning, placed their stamp on students of color by calling them "high risk." This risk concept and other terms, once again, were born out of the feeling that minorities are outside the regular educational track and are always a gamble for a White university. In addition, many of the programs were built around a type of "deficit model" so that, without fine diagnostic tools and procedures, these students were assumed not to be able to survive. Indeed, the climate of support for some African American, Latino, and other students of color was often so psychologically toxic, coupled with special minority programs that were isolated and marginalized from the mainstream of the academy, that one could predict that some special program students would fail.

A great deal of research has been conducted related to the issue of failure, in general, and failure related to African American students and other underrepresented college groups, in particular. Tinto's (1993) theory of student departure from institutions of higher education focuses on the role they play in influencing the social and intellectual development of their students. Tinto (1993) and McHale (1997) both assert that students come to college with varying personal, family, and academic characteristics and skills, including initial dispositions, intentions, and commitments with regard to college attendance and personal goals. These intentions and commitments are modified continually over time through a series of interactions between the student and the structures and members of the academic and social systems of the college (Pascarella and Terenzini 1991). Satisfying and rewarding encounters lead to greater integration and thus to student retention (Pascarella and Terenzini 1991; McHale 1997).

We are now moving into a new century, and the experiences of some African Americans, Hispanic/Latinos, Native Americans, Asian Americans, and, yes, many low-income White Americans, illustrate the struggle to maintain themselves against the barriers to higher education. We deliberately use the word "some" minority students, because it would be a mistake to assume we are talking about "all." And yet, in the face of these psycho-social and economic barriers, policy makers, such as those found among the Regents of the University of California system, and some of their political allies are reaching back to challenge the gains advanced by affirmative action legislation. Thus, the affirmative action debate is yet another factor to add to the issues faced by some students throughout the history of this country. In this paper, we refer to many of these policies and socio-economic factors as barriers to educational success.

Barriers to Educational Success

Although some are inadequately prepared, there has always been a high level of unrealized potential among students of color. Opportunity programs for young people have always functioned best as arenas for identifying and recruiting talented minority youth. Because of individual histories that often include substandard living conditions, inadequate schools, and exposure to antisocial attitudes bred by discrimination, many young minority group members carry with them a number of barriers to receiving the benefits of higher education.

These barriers to education fall under six different rubrics (Allen 1977): academic, financial, aspirational, psychological, geographic, and sociological. Although all of these barriers contribute to the probability of educational failure, the three most serious are the academic, financial, and aspirational. Consequently, in order to attack the roots of academic failure, it is crucial to address these principal obstructions to success (Robinson 1990; Levin and Levin 1991).

Academic barriers stem directly from the poor training many minority students receive in the schools they attended while growing up. Inner-city schools, in particular, often literally crumbling, fail to provide an atmosphere that encourages academic pursuits. Sometimes the mere problem of physical survival simply overshadows the ostensible purposes of education. The curriculum in these schools may leave something to be desired, as well, by failing to focus on the places where the interests of the students intersect with educational goals. In addition, placement and advancement in primary and secondary schools is often driven by testing, which places minority students at a disadvantage. All of these factors combine to produce a climate that is unwholesome not only for students' minds, but for their bodies, as well. Students who associate education with environments that are literally dangerous, with teaching that ignores their cultural and social orientation, and with forms of testing that sometimes seem designed to deny them will probably not find the transition to college an easy one.

The financial barriers faced by many minority students are too well known to require extensive documentation. Poverty is a powerful obstacle both to actual learning and to matriculation within the educational structure (Robinson 1990). Limited family incomes function in many ways to reduce a child's chances at school. It is erroneously assumed that low income minority parents do not attempt to foster educational aspirations in their children (Tidwell 1989). Nevertheless, a lack of resources translates into a lack of exposure to many kinds of opportunity, including those related to education. Some low-income parents are likely to have suffered from limited access to education themselves; for that reason, they cannot function well as a source of either information or school related training. The child from a background of poverty, is unlikely to grow up with the books, the trips to museums, and other extracurricular educational experiences with which middle class families can supply their children. A lack of reliable transportation, which is a typical feature of poverty, not only reduces or eliminates visits to the library, but may also interfere with a child's chances of making it to school on time. For these reasons, even those minority young people who do attend college are frequently products of a background that has systematically deprived them of the rudimentary training expected of an entering freshman. Unfortunately, economic conditions have gotten worse in the last decade for members of minority groups, guaranteeing that poverty will continue to exercise its negative effects on education.

Perhaps the most significant barrier to education, one that lies beyond the more material disadvantages they may experience at school or at home, is the absence of educational aspirations that too often characterizes the attitudes of young minority group members (Fordham and Ogbu 1986). That minority students' attitudes can interfere with their educational attainment is particularly distressing because they usually have a strong desire to finish college.

The short-term and long-term goals some African American students bring with them to college, however, frequently compete directly with goals consistent with learning and with staying in college. Given a lack of exposure to other possibilities, it may be especially hard for these students to focus on those activities that will ensure their successful adjustment to college life. At the other end of the spectrum, having grown up in communities where many of the adults must struggle against seemingly insurmountable odds, young minority group members, many of whom come from impoverished backgrounds, may have little experience imagining themselves succeeding. Without an image of success, they can find it difficult to set high goals for the future, such as completing college or having the kind of job for which college is a prerequisite.

Remedies for Failure

Because education is the keystone to economic success for so many African Americans and other people of color, society must address the factors that limit success in college. Those charged with bringing disadvantaged youngsters into the educational process must also continue to improve their techniques and expand their efforts. Programs designed to raise educational aspirations in poor and minority communities may slowly raise the internal standards against which low income students of color measure themselves and against which they are measured by others. Nevertheless, the absence of a national commitment to improving access to education, a commitment of both funding and institutional support, bodes ill for a relatively rapid increase in the numbers of low income students of color entering college and finishing with a degree.

Programs designed to increase minority participation in higher education have had some positive effect. As college and high school educators gain more experience in guiding minority youngsters toward a college education, some of the social and attitudinal barriers should decline in importance (Bennett and Okinaka 1990; Levin and Levin 1991). As Tidwell (1988) suggested, the principal responsibility for identifying talented young people and assuring that they attain high educational goals falls upon secondary school teachers and counselors. That task has two components: identifying students with the emotional characteristics that support academic success and finding ways to change attitudes that interfere with an interest in academic pursuits.

Because college may make unfamiliar demands on some young people coming from a minority community, academic success demands more than academic ability. Therefore, a young person with "emotional intelligence" stands a better chance of success in college than does one without the emotional qualities to sustain him or her during a difficult period of transition (Sedlacek and Webster 1978). Those minority group members who succeed in college are likely to have a positive self-image that supports realistic self-appraisal, a good grasp of ideas and techniques for dealing with racism, a focus on the future, and leadership skills. A young person who has these characteristics may still come in conflict with peer group values that denigrate community involvement and academic achievement. Frequently, talented minority students can benefit greatly from the help of a high school counselor in negotiating emotional and social obstacles and in perceiving their educational achievements in a positive light.

Attitude change is crucial to the educational success of minority group members. The work of high school and college counselors with individual students fits closely with the work of programs intended to translate parents' educational aspirations for their children into realistic expectations of educational success. In addition, students who perceive their relationship with predominantly white institutions of higher education as part of an internal struggle with racial identity may have great difficulty in acclimating to the demands of that environment. The Civil Rights struggle taught that an approach yoking demands for radical overhaul of society with a willingness to work within the system actually can achieve change, however slowly.

Events on campus can constantly remind African American and other students of color that the socialization processes of White Americans permeate the structure of college life. Nevertheless, those who balance an enlightened awareness of the effects of racism, past and present, with a genuine desire to engage with the larger community on campus and beyond stand a better chance of meeting both their individual goals and those of the communities from which they come. Colleges and universities may eventually learn to meet members of minority groups halfway. Unfortunately, the situation at present demands that, without releasing pressure for change, minority students must be the ones to do the lion's share of accommodating.

Although the responsibility for engaging with the majority community in a positive way falls inevitably, albeit unfairly, on the shoulders of minority students, it is incumbent on institutions of higher education and on society in general to attack the systematic indifference and hostility minority group students regularly encounter on college campuses. Indeed, the present retreat from a commitment to affirmative action signifies to some minority group members a scaled-down commitment on the part of the larger society to repair the damage wrought for centuries by slavery and racism. Unless the critical need to bring young minority group members into the system receives adequate recognition and support from social and governmental institutions, even the slow progress realized in the recent past may come to a halt.

References

Allen, A. 1977. Educational opportunities programs for minority and low-income students in California and U.S. colleges. Unpublished doctoral dissertation, University of California, Los Angeles.

Bennett, C., and A.M. Okinaka. 1990. Factors related to persistence among Asian, Black, Hispanic, and White undergraduates at a predominantly White university: Comparison between first and fourth year cohorts. *The Urban Review* 22: 33–60.

Fordham, S., and J.U. Ogbu. 1986. Black students' school success: Coping with the "burden of 'acting White.'" *The Urban Review* 18: 176–206.

Levin, M.E., and J.R. Levin. 1991. A critical examination of academic retention programs for at-risk minority college students. *Journal of College Student Development* 32: 323–334.

McHale, M. 1997. The impact of an intervention program on the academic and retention of students in academic difficulty. Unpublished doctoral dissertation proposal, University of California, Los Angeles.

Pascarella, E., and P. Terenzini, P. 1991. Predicting voluntary freshman persistence/withdrawal behavior in a residential university: A path analytic validation of Tinto's model. *Journal of Educational Psychology* 75: 215–226.

Pinkney, A. 1975. *Black Americans.* New Jersey: Prentice-Hall.

Robinson, T. 1990. Understanding the gap between entry and exit: A cohort analysis of African American students' persistence. *Journal of Negro Education* 59: 207–218.

Sedlacek, W. E., and D.W. Webster. 1978. Admission and retention of minority students in large universities. *Journal of College Student Personnel* 19: 242–248.

Tidwell, R. 1988. The addition of counseling staff at racially isolated schools: An assessment by students and counselors. *Journal of Counseling and Development* 66: 342–344.

Tidwell, R. 1989. Academic success and the school dropout: A minority perspective. In *Black students: Psychosocial issues and academic achievement*, edited by G.L. Berry and J.K. Asamen. Newbury Park, CA: Publications, Inc.

Tidwell, R., and G.L. Berry. 1993. Higher education and the African-American experience: Historical perceptions and the challenge for change. *College Student Journal* 27: 465–471.

Tinto, V. 1993. *Leaving college: Rethinking the causes and curls of student attrition.* Chicago: University of Chicago Press.

Weinberg, M. 1977. *A chance to learn: A history of race and education in the United States.* London: Cambridge University Press.

Wilson, R. 1994. Minorities in higher education. In *Minorities in higher education,* edited by M.J. Justy, R. Wilson, and L. Björk. Washington, DC: American Council on Education, Oryx Press.

6

The Nursing Profession and Minority Populations

Freida Hopkins Outlaw, DNSc, RN, CS

Recruitment and Retention

Kem B. Louie, PhD, RN, CS, FAAN

Status of Nursing Among Minority Populations Asian and Pacific Islander Americans (APIAs)

Audrey Koertvelyessy, MSN, RN, PNP

The Status of Nursing among Minority Populations: Focus of the American Indian/Alaskan Natives

Lisa Cruz-Avalos, MSN, RN, CS

Hispanic Representation in Nursing

Freida Hopkins Outlaw, DNSc, RN,CS

Recruitment and Retention

According to the U.S. Bureau of Census, by the year 2000 people of color—among them people of African decent, Hispanics, Asians and Native Americans—will comprise more than half of the racial, ethnic, and culturally diverse groups in this country (Andrews 1992, 7). By the year 2080 these peoples of color will comprise 51.1 percent of the total American population so that approximately one in every three persons in the United States will have originated from one of these groups (Andrews 1993; Blank and Slipp 1995; Campinha-Bacote 1996).These dramatic changes in demographics will require that nurses be prepared to meet the health care needs of all patients that they will be called upon to serve. Currently, however, there is a dearth of knowledge about the health care beliefs, values, and needs of the diverse cultural, racial, and ethnic groups that are the consumers of health services.

Nursing has a history of underrepresentation of people of color in the profession. According to Barbee (1993) and Bessent (1989), the nursing profession has been populated primarily with white, middle-class women. However, having been brought to America as slaves, black women were given the role of health care providers on plantations, a role which they continued to fulfill even after slavery was abolished (Hine 1989). According to Carnegie (1986), although these women were not formally identified as nurses, the roles they assumed—lay midwives who delivered babies both black and white; taking care of the sick in the families that owned them; providing care for sick slaves and their sick family members—certainly were within the scope of nursing. However, for many social, political, and economic reasons, there remains an underrepresentation of nurses of color in professional nursing.

Hine (1989) posits that nurses of color are the link to improvement in the health care of patients over the last several decades because it has been nurses, rather than physicians, who have understood and treated patients in the social context in which patients live. She further speculates that the minuscule improvements in the health of people of color in this society are directly correlated to the small numbers of nurses of color found in professional nursing.

It is to be noted that the argument is not that nurses of color are the only nurses who can render health care to minority populations. However, with growing populations of people of color, and with the shift of health care from hospital-based to community-based care combined with the bleak health report of minority people, the necessity of having increased representation of nurses of color providing clinical services, conducting research, and teaching future generations of nurses becomes significantly connected to the health outcomes of patients of color (Greer 1995; National Advisory Council on Nurse Education and Practice 1996).

Accepting the premise that nurses of color do not have to provide all of the care to patients like themselves, it has been suggested that the recruitment and retention in nursing of persons of racial and ethnic minority groups is a primary strategy for improving the health care of ethnically, racially, and culturally diverse groups of patients who are often poor and disfranchised members of society. What is important about these groups of nurses is that, while not true of them alone, they are often more familiar with the communities where large numbers of poor minority patients live, are more inclined to work in such communities, and thus are more likely to have a positive impact in them (Greer 1995). Powell (1992) points out that African American nurses, more than white nurses, chose to serve in black communities. She also posits that they are often more aware of the problems that underserved, poor populations of people experience.

In the area of research, Jackson argues that conformity to white middle-class standards drives the thinking and training of nurses, which influences the research perspective of most nurses. She calls this approach to nursing research, in which the thinking is a form of "decontextualized individualism" instead of a "contextualized" approach, the "whiting-out of difference" in nursing research (Jackson 1993, 376). This approach begins with the conceptualization of the research and ends with the research report in which minority viewpoints are marginalized to the extent that, usually, information about minorities is not included in the findings. Jackson believes that simply including minority groups in study samples does not ensure that the research has any relevance for minority populations because individualistic, decontextualized, not sociocultural, approaches dominate the interpretations of the findings that have influenced most nursing research.

The predominant research method when group researchers from dominant racial/ethnic and cultural groups are conducting research focused on people of color usually involves studies comparing white and black samples where the differences between the two groups are highlighted. Prime examples of this conceptually and methodologically flawed research are early empirical studies on African American families in which low-socioeconomic black families were compared to middle-class white families and the differences found between them attributed to race, not socioeconomic factors (Myers 1982). As a result, these comparative studies yielded findings that were interpreted in a way to support Deficit Model Theories often used to explain the health beliefs, values, and behaviors of people of color. Interventions based on these findings often are misguided and are not therapeutic for the populations they have been developed to serve. For these reasons many researchers of color are calling for research that is focused on the heterogeneity among minority groups in order to increase specific knowledge of the health care needs of minority patients in the context of the world in which they live (Davis 1992; Outlaw 1995; Phillips 1995; Porter & Villarruel 1993).

Nurse researchers of color in general believe that they have an obligation to do research specifically aimed at examining the health needs of people of color (Davis 1992). This obligation is the primary objective of the American Nurses Association Ethnic Racial Minority Fellowship Program: to create a cadre of nurse researchers of color. Over the years that this program has been operative, the largest pool to date of doctorally prepared nurses of color has been produced. These nurses have influenced agendas aimed at developing programs of research that are culturally sensitive and attuned to issues that are of grave importance to the health of minority communities.

Porter and Villarruel (1993) assert that nurse researchers are bound by their professionalism to conduct research, interpret findings, and disseminate the results of their research as accurately as they can, which means that they reflect in their research the complex and often diverse realities of people of color. In order to accomplish the task of moving from unicultural thinking to examining phenomena of interest to nursing with awareness of the diversities of cultural settings that inform the lives of patients of color, there must be an increase in the numbers of nurse researchers from these diverse communities. As evidence of minority nurses's commitment to the problems of ethnically, racially, and culturally diverse populations, Jackson (1993) found that the *Journal of the Black Nurses Association* contained 25 percent of the studies focused on the health of African Americans.

Finally, in regards to research, minority nurses are needed to develop and participate in partnerships in minority communities to ensure that the research that is conducted is "with the black community and not on the black community" (Phillips 1995, 26). Phillips believes the creation of a cadre of minority nurses who can play a vital role developing and implementing research agendas in minority communities will assist in dispelling mistrust that is a legacy of episodes such as the Tuskegee Syphilis Experiment, in which government researchers withheld treatment from black men who had been diagnosed with syphilis in order to study the effects of syphilis on their bodies. This horrendous episode, more so than similar ones, has led persons in minority communities to be very mistrustful of research, often to their disadvantage since the presence of persons from minority populations in clinical trials of new and innovative treatments for life-threatening diseases remains discouragingly small.

Few would argue that in order to improve the health status of people of color a variety of avenues for conducting culturally-sensitive research have to be established. According to Phillips (1995), nurses of color are in a unique position to conduct the research that examines a plethora of health issues of concern to minority communities. However, to establish a career as a researcher, education at the doctoral level is essential. In fact, the current trend is for doctorally-prepared nurses to enhance their research skills by being mentored by an established researcher. This model has been purported to be crucial to the development of researchers of color because it allows them an opportunity to increase their research skills and to demonstrate their abilities in academic settings heavily involved in research thereby enhancing their opportunities to be included in networks that have been previously closed to them (May, Meleis, and Winstead-Fry 1982; Outlaw 1995; Williams and Blackburn 1988).The imperative, then, is to create more doctorally-prepared nurses of color to conduct nursing research that is ideologically relevant for patients of color.

In order to have more doctorally-prepared nurses, however, the pool of prepared nurses have to be enhanced through the recruitment, retention, and graduation of nurses of color. Additionally, these nurses, starting at the generic level, have to be infused with the idea that it will be their legacies of contribution to clinical, educational, and research leadership that will be needed to insure that people of color are assured health care that is appropriately culturally sensitive, and that, as health care providers, they are sufficiently competent to orchestrate that care in whatever venue they choose to devote themselves: research, practice, and/or education.

This chapter will describe those groups of minorities that are underrepresented in nursing, discuss their characteristics, and identify barriers that members of these groups may encounter when seeking to become educated as professional nurses. Finally, recommendations will be offered for the recruitment, retention, and education of members of these minority groups who aspire to become professional nurses.

Demographics: Black Americans

Black Americans are comprised of African Americans, Africans, Haitians, Caribbean West Indians, Black Cubans, Black Hispanics, and other groups whose ancestors originated in Africa. To be African American literally means that the American continent is the origin of your birth and generally of your immediate ancestors (Hacker 1995). Other ethnic groups of African descent (hence "black") in America, such as West Indians or Haitians, generally distinguish themselves from African Americans, often preferring to acknowledge equally the French or British cultural influences which make them different from Americans (Hacker 1995).

One of the ways that differences between African Americans and West Indians may be noted is the nature of experiences of, and reactions to, racism by persons in the two ethnic groups. While most adult African Americans will readily acknowledge that they have experienced racist acts and invidious discrimination, adult West Indians generally deny that racism exists in the West Indies. Gopaul-McNicol (1993) posits that this denial is related to the fact that 80 to 90 percent of the population of the West Indies (with the exception of Trinidad and Guyana) are people of African descent. Consequently, these persons tend to have few experiences of anti-black racism. And while some among them admit that some visages of racism remain in the West Indies, it has been determined that the forms and experiences are less insidious than what is experienced by people of African descent in the United States (Gopaul-McNicol 1993).

It must be recognized, then, that people of African descent are widely dispersed in a variety of socioeconomic and cultural settings, and do not make up a homogeneous racial group. Rather, we are an ethnically, thus culturally, diverse dispersed racial population. Bearing this in mind, throughout this essay the term "black" will be used, when appropriate, to speak of this population as one inclusive of all ethnic groups that trace defining aspects of their cultural and genealogical ancestries to Africa.

When considering issues of recruiting and retaining persons of African descent in programs of nursing education, the importance of recognizing differences among various subgroups of people of color of African descent becomes readily apparent when the misguided belief that all black people, regardless of their particular ethnicity, have the same values, beliefs, and behaviors as a result of sharing a single cultural orientation. It is not uncommon to see in the literature essays about "the black family" or "the cultural aspects of African Americans." When nursing recruitment and retention strategies are being developed for people of African descent, it is imperative that the heterogeneity of the racial group be taken into account and that the persons being recruited or retained not be approached as though they belong to a monolithic population.

According to the 1990 census, Black Americans comprise 12.1 percent of the total population of the United States and are projected to account for approximately 12.3 per-cent of the population by the year 2000 (Hacker 1995). Although Hispanics, Asians, Native Americans, and Hawaiians are growing faster than Black Americans, black people continue to grow by about half a percentage point each decade (Hacker 1995). By the year 2050, one in eight Americans will be a person of African decent (Philadelphia Inquirer 1997).

A significant factor that has distinguished black Americans from ethnic groups of other races is their legacy of suffering invidious discrimination growing out of racialized enslavement, which was predicated, in significant part, on "science"-validated and religion-blessed presumptions of black racial inferiority and white racial superiority. Being "black" was both the sign and symbol of this presumed inferiority. This color-coded stigma continues to condition the lives of persons of African descent in the United States. Significantly lower levels of educational achievement by persons of African descent compared to persons of European descent can be attributed, to a significant extent (though not totally), to direct and indirect effects of racial discrimination against persons of African descent and discrimination in favor of persons of European descent.

Efforts to recruit and retain students of nursing who are of African descent are devoted to countering the effects of inappropriate racial discrimination (i.e., discrimination premised on and supportive of black racial inferiority and white racial superiority). However, such efforts must not be focused exclusively on identifying and seeking to eliminate racial discrimination. In order to have a pool of candidates that are able to meet the rigorous requirements of a nursing education curriculum, a clear and unequivocal commitment will have to be made to find potential students who are persons of color who are willing as well as able to master challenging course work in the natural sciences such as chemistry, as well as courses in the social sciences and the humanities. All involved in and devoted to efforts to increase the numbers of persons of color providing health care in this country must do so with commitment to the understanding that there is no inherent conflict between these efforts and commitment to maintaining the highest standards by which students are assessed as they progress through and complete programs in nursing education.

The health status of black Americans is in crisis (Hale 1992; Phillips 1995). According to Phillips (1995), there are two reasons for the abominable health status of black Americans: the large numbers of uninsured black people; and the disproportionately heavy burden of illness that they suffer. Some of the heavy burden that African Americans experience is a result of their continuous exposure to racism and discrimination, putting them at increased risk for developing physical and psychological illnesses (Billingsley 1992; Lloyd 1980; Outlaw 1993). African Americans suffer disproportionately from hypertension, cardiac disease, obesity, stroke, lung cancer, and alcohol and drug abuse (Billingsley 1992; Hale 1992; Outlaw 1993). These are all preventable diseases that are linked inextricably to stress. The rate of infant mortality among black Americans is also twice the rate among white Americans. Finally, the number of HIV/AIDS cases is raising faster among African Americans, specifically adolescent women (Avery 1992; Elders 1995) than among white Americans. The many direct and indirect effects of invidious racial discrimination experienced by persons of African descent are a major source of near continuous stress in their lives.

In this context, the underrepresentation of black nurses greatly impacts the quality of culturally sensitive and competent nursing care delivered to black patients (AAN Expert Panel 1992; Elders 1995; Greer 1995). Greer has called for black nurses to be the primary health care providers in their own communities in order to effect real change in the health status of people of color, black people in particular, who live in the areas in which nurse-managed primary health care centers are becoming the future model for delivering health care. Hine (1989) has found that, historically, an important factor that has differentiated black nurses from white nurses is the expectation on the part of persons in black communities that individual black nurses will be practitioners in their communities and thus help to improve the health of their people. That health care in this country is moving swiftly from inpatient hospitals to community-based care has been well established (National Advisory Council on

Nurse Education and Practice 1996; National League for Nursing 1995). Therefore, the time has come for black nurses to fulfill the expectations of members of black communities that they "be patient and race advocates, constantly seeking improved health care" (Hine 1989, 188). Understanding the expectations in black communities regarding by whom and how health care should be delivered must influence, in appropriate ways, efforts to recruit, retain, and graduate African Americans, and others persons of color, from undergraduate, Masters, and doctoral-level nursing programs.

The Status of Black Nurses in the Workforce: The Connection to Recruitment and Retention

Nursing has led the movement from hospital-based care to community-based care. In part, this movement has been fueled by nursing's philosophical commitment that an essential part of nursing is its focus on primary prevention. Given black communities's historical expectations of black nurses as trusted care givers, it behooves nursing, in order to operationalize its agenda of providing high quality care in urban communities, to embrace with conviction, not with grudging reluctance, that nurses of color will have to be recognized as a vital part of community-based care endeavors. To this end, there has to be a concerted effort by leaders of nursing to increase at all levels the number of nurses of color. According to statistics complied by the Division of Nursing, as of March 1996, there were 2,558,874 licensed registered nurses. Approximately eighty percent of these nurses are employed in nursing (Division of Nursing 1996). Of these practicing nurses, they estimate that 107,527, or 4.2 percent, are black nurses. The National Advisory Council on Nurse Education and Practice (1996) stated that minorities are underrepresented in nursing: that is, the proportion of nurses of color is substantially less the numbers of persons of color in this country. They also postulated that if current trends continue into the future, the numbers of nurses from racial and ethnic groups of color will not increase significantly.

Enrollments of persons from these groups increased by a slight percentage in programs that prepared people to be licensed as registered nurses, and these increases occurred across groups with the exception of American Indians, who remained stable (National League of Nursing 1995). However, while the percentage of graduations from RN programs between 1993 and 1994 for Hispanics and Asians rose slightly, graduation rates for black nursing students remained stable. Of further note, black nursing students are more likely to be enrolled in associate degree programs than in diploma or baccalaureate programs (Powell 1992). This might well be a result of the how associate degree programs were initially marketed to various racial and ethnic populations from which students were then recruited. For many licensed practical nurses, associate degree nursing programs were initially presented as the means by which they might obtain their RN and thus become full nurse professionals.

Of black nurses that are enrolled in generic baccalaureate programs, the majority attend and graduate from historically black colleges and universities. Powell (1992) analyzed the 1991 National League of Nursing data and found that approximately 25 percent of black nurses graduated from historically black colleges and universities, and 400 other predominately white institutions graduated on average 2.8 undergraduate nursing students each year.

Recruitment and Retention of Black Nurses: Impediments and Solutions

Black Americans generally have always placed a high premium on and have believed in the efficacy of education (Billingsley 1992). The literature, for example, is replete with examples of mothers and fathers in slavery risking their lives in order to learn to read and write or to have their children be taught to read and write. Further examples of these commitments can be seen in black churches where scholarship programs to assist college students are a regular part of church cultures. Often when I am interviewing single mothers about their aspirations for their children, they often say they want their child or children "to get a good education."

However, there are barriers that often impede, in particular, the efforts of urban black children, their parents, and other members of extended family and community support networks toward achieving their educational goals. Some of these barriers are problems within educational systems such as invidious stereotypes held by teachers regarding what black children are capable of learning and how they can be expected to behave. These stereotypes influence in significant ways, often unintentionally, how these teachers teach, interact with, and influence their students. Other school system factors that impact negatively on black children are "the hidden curriculum, the influence of environmental factors, teacher expectations, and the lack of parent advocacy" (Gopaul-McNicol 1993, 64).

In order to entice black children to become interested in careers in nursing, impediments created by poor primary and secondary education have to be eliminated. Programs must be developed or refined, and if in place, enhanced and maintained, that encourage students at an early age to excel in the sciences and in other academic courses that will be needed for them to pursue a nursing career. Further, schools of nursing need to develop programs that can be a part of the outreach of their primary health care centers. Such outreach efforts need to be developed that target elementary, middle, and high schools in order to educate students about the benefits of a career in nursing. The important point is that programs that are developed to encourage students in urban settings to consider nursing as a career option have to start in the elementary schools where students can be provided the additional help they need in order to be successful in school. Colleges and universities must then be encouraged to adopt inner-city schools in which students are tutored and mentored with regard to choosing careers. In order to stimulate young inner-city students to become interested in nursing as a career, nursing organizations and programs must form partnerships with urban elementary schools to create programs aimed at encouraging students to consider nursing.

One such program, developed in a predominately white university located in a heavily minority urban community, is the "Take a Child to Work Program." A day at the University with a nursing professor is arranged for students in middle-school who have expressed an interest in nursing as a career possibility. A program of this kind can also include the primary health care centers that are operated by many nursing schools: they can be sites where students spend a day with an advanced practice nurse observing them deliver integrated primary health care. This type of role modeling is necessary since students are often unaware of the independent nature of nursing and of the variety of career choices available to nurses. According to Greer (1995) role modeling is one of the ways of redressing the under-representation of black people in Nursing.

Parents of elementary school children also need to be informed of the many options that nursing as a career can provide. Additionally, they need to be informed of the rigorous academic preparation that a nursing education demands. If these parents have as a goal early in the educational life of their child that she or he be educated to realize her or his potential to the fullest extent possible, they can be more of an advocate for the child in the school system. Aponte (1994) identifies efforts such as those involving families, schools, and programs represented by nursing schools or nursing clinics as ones that fulfill what he terms an "ecostructural paradigm," a most apt model, in his judgment, for working successfully with poor, often minority families.

Historically, many persons in black communities have thought of black nurses as respectable and responsible health care providers (Hine 1989). In fact, Hine (1989) states that black communities in general have viewed the nursing profession with more favor than they have physicians. The most salient reason for this perception is that nurses have traditionally worked in these communities, and have been very responsive and supportive of their health needs. Over time, however, the status of nursing as a career has eroded in many black communities. There are multiple reasons for this erosion, including the unprofessional portrayal of nurses on television and in movies. Further, nursing in many respects, is considered "women's work." Over the last two decades there has been disdain in black communities for occupations that were considered designated for women.

In many urban black communities where there is a plethora of unskilled workers, many people have nonprofessional jobs in hospitals and other health care facilities such as nursing homes. Because they work in health care facilities and often wear white uniforms they are perceived as nurses in their communities. These persons, however, are not perceived as professionals in their worksettings. Additionally, most black churches include a nursing guild as part of the church's organizational structure. Many of the women who make up this guild wear white uniforms, including a white nursing cape and cap. However, they are seldom professional nurses, and usually their duties consist primarily of insuring that the pastor receives liquids after the sermon and that persons attending and participating in services are attended to should they be overcome by The Spirit. What this means, however, is that many elements of these communities have claimed nursing as their venue and in the process diminished the valued perception of nursing as a profession based on formal, scholarly education and training, one in which people are in control of their own practice and in which one needs to excel academically. Parents also need to be informed about career mobility, competitive salaries, and job flexibilities that a career in nursing can make available to their child.

Greer (1995) identifies several possible solutions for the problem of under-representation of black people in nursing. She called for commitment to this goal on the part of civic organizations, businesses, hospitals, and other health care organizations, and on the part of schools of nursing, to develop programs for black students in the schools that introduce them to nursing. Appropriate commitment on the part of all of these institutions will require, as well, a greater infusion of financial and human resources into programs aimed at recruiting and retaining black students at all levels of nursing education.

Recruitment efforts need also to develop new paradigms. That is—and this is a focal point of this essay—efforts should be directed toward creating opportunities for black people, in particular, to enter nursing. For example, schools of nursing with progressive masters programs and competitive doctoral programs should develop recruitment strategies aimed at identifying and recruiting black students who are in the top tier of their graduating classes, who have high SAT scores and who are National Merit Scholars or have achieved similar recognitions. Successful innovative programs, such as one developed by Florida A&M University, should be investigated to discover how they have implemented successfully a program aimed at attracting black National Merit Scholars. Black students with these types of academic profiles need to be mentored to continue their education until they obtain their doctoral degrees. These students should form the core of the future black nursing clinical scholars, researchers, and educators.

Secondly, black students who are interested in nursing as a career need to be mentored about the academic profiles needed to enter nursing. Additionally, more programs that have been developed, such as that at Southern University School of Nursing, are needed to target individuals who are first generation college students and who wish to become nurses but need enhancement of their educational skills. These students also usually need practical guidance regarding how to manage time, how to study, as well as how to manage the mundane factors related to being a successful college student in a demanding institution.

Finally, and most importantly, honest and thorough evaluations of students's skills have to be done by mentors so that students are properly counseled about identifying and choosing educational situations in which they can be most successful. For example, it is no accident that Powell (1992) found that historically black colleges and universities (HBCU) graduate a high proportion of the baccalaureate-prepared black nurses currently in the workforce. The explicit mission of HBCU's has been the provision of academic support, spiritual guidance, and intense nurturing that black students often need, especially if they are the first person from their family to attend college.

Black students who attend predominately white institutions often need similar support from their advisors and mentors for a number of important reasons. Some colleges and universities have recognized this fact and have instituted mentorship programs in which black students are assigned, in addition to an academic advisor, a black nurse mentor whom they can count on for guidance and support throughout their academic career. More of these types of programs need to be developed and their effectiveness evaluated to ascertain how they can be continuously improved to meet the needs of a changing population of black students.

Both Greer (1995) and Outlaw (1995) identified the need for black nurses at all levels of the educational process in nursing to have one or more mentors. The literature on mentoring is replete with the idea that the most successful mentoring relationships occur when there is congruence in such factors as personal characteristics, including gender, race, and ethnicity (Campbell-Heider 1986; Megel 1985). Therefore, national databases that identify black nurses and their achievements are a vital source that need to be used to create networks of researchers with similar research interests, and of nurses who can work with community organizations to identify potentially talented students. Data from these databases will be valuable for other purposes, as well, among them supporting efforts to enhance the recruitment into and retention of black students in programs of nursing education.

Finally, successful second-degree black students need to be targeted as potential recruits to enter the field of nursing. They have already demonstrated that they can successfully complete an academic program. As potential nurses, then, they will already possess the study skills, motivation, and maturity regarding goals and what it takes to achieve what we would expect of students of advanced nursing education. In the case of black students, those who have graduated from majority colleges and universities have also demonstrated that they can problem-solve and, very likely, that they have coped successfully with institutional and individual racism that is often encountered by students of color in predominantly white institutions.

Financial barriers are also commonplace for students of color. Outlaw (1995) found that, in the case of postdoctoral students, financial constraints, and the related pragmatics of life, often determined, ultimately, whether students of color could accept a postdoctoral fellowship. Adequate financial support for black nursing students was also identified by Powell (1992) as an important challenge that must be overcome if black students are going to be recruited and retained in nursing education programs. Often black students are not only responsible for their own financial well-being, but in many instances they are expected to contribute to meeting the financial obligations of their families of origin. Additionally, black women who are second-degree students are sometimes single parents with households to manage financially while in school. It is estimated that in 1982 approximately 49 percent of black family households were headed by females (Giger and Davidhizar 1991). With respect to two-parent black households in which one of the parents is a nursing student, there is a high probability that the student will need additional financial support because often the other wage earner does not earn enough salary to support the family. For example, Giger and Davidhizer reported that "the salary of a Black man with a 4-year college degree was comparable to the salary of a White man with only 9 to 11 years of education" (Giger and Davidhizer 1991, 155). With such disparities in salaries between the two racial groups, and without adequate financial support from colleges and universities that are recruiting black nursing students an additional burden is more likely to be faced by students of color than other, more affluent, particularly white, students.

Black organizations need to commit to developing long-term financial plans devoted to addressing some of the financial needs of qualified black students interested in careers in nursing. However, major financial commitments need to be developed by nursing schools that recognize and accept their obligation to prepare nurses of color who can add substantially to the rapidly changing health care agendas that are becoming more community-based. When Greer (1995) identified commitment as one of the criteria to be met in combating the under-representation of black people in nursing, financial commitment was recognized as one of the essential components of a successful recruitment and retention program aimed at increasing black presence in nursing.

In sum, there should be a variety of recruitment and retention strategies designed and devoted to increasing black student enrollment in undergraduate, masters, and doctoral levels of nursing education as well as to ensure retention in and graduation from these programs. These strategies must include all of the essential elements identified by Greer (1995) if they are to change the underrepresentation of black nurses in nursing. Greer identified recruitment, mentoring, educational support, commitment, and role-modeling as the essential components of a recruitment and retention program aimed at increasing the numbers of blacks in nursing. Institutions with nursing programs, and organizations committed to nursing and to changing for the better the demographics of the nursing profession, must design and implement programs that include all of these elements.

Kem B. Louie,
PhD, RN,CS, FAAN

Status of Nursing among Minority Populations Asian and Pacific Islander Americans (APIAs)

Demographic Information of APIAs

Asian and Pacific Islander Americans (APIAs) have been identified as the fastest growing minority group in the United States during the last twenty years. From 1980 to 1990, APIAs more than doubled in number, rising from 3,773,233, or 1.5 percent of the total population to 7,273,662 or 2.9 percent of the population in 1990 (Lin-Fu 1993). Furthermore, this escalation is expected to double again by the year 2009. The increase in APIA immigrants is due to the repeal of the anti-immigrant law toward Asians by President Kennedy in 1965. Today, the majority of the APIA population in the United States is immigrants and refugees who have entered the United States in the last 25 years. In 1990, 95 percent of the populations were Asian Americans while 5 percent were Pacific Islanders. These subgroups include Chinese (23.8 percent), Filipinos (20.4 percent), Japanese (12.3 percent), Asian Indians (11.8 percent), Korean (11.6 percent) and Vietnamese (8.9 percent). Among Pacific Islander Americans, Hawaiians comprised 57.8 percent of the population. Together with Samoans, Guamanians and Togans, they make up 93.4 percent of Pacific Islander Americans. The majority of the Asian American and Pacific Islanders reside in urban cities predominately located on the East and West coasts. A majority of the Pacific Islanders reside in the Pacific basin. The largest number of Pacific Islanders located in the U.S. mainland reside in California.

There are more than 7.4 million Americans of Asian descent and this group is composed of more than 20 subgroups, each with its own historical background, language, religion, and history of immigration. Some of the subgroups have little in common with each other in terms of language, culture, or health problems. Asian and Pacific Islander Americans are generally viewed by society as monolithic. It is important to realize that in order to provide appropriate health care services and increase the efforts to include this diverse group in the nursing profession, the differences between these subgroups must be understood. Improve the health status of APIAs requires the understanding of the cultural and behavioral norms as well as biomedical issues relevant to each distinct ethnic group.

Only recent efforts have been made to understand the health status of this diverse group by federal agencies. Guillermo (1994) reports that the publication, *Healthy People 2000-Objectives for the Nation* and the Minority Health Improvement Act were to provide opportunities for minority and health professionals. She notes that the objectives were predominately targeted to other minority groups rather than Asian and Pacific Islander Americans. She believes there is intent to exclude this group of minorities from entering the health field because of the current belief that Asians and Pacific Islanders are overrepresented in the health professions. This belief is based upon the collection of aggregated data of APIAs and limited methodology. These results suggest there is a sufficient supply of Asians and Pacific Islander health professionals to serve this population. A number of ethnic subgroups of APIA health professionals is still needed.

The health status of APIAs has recently been reviewed by Chen and Hawks (1995). They found an increase in the incidence of lung cancer, cardiovascular disease, Hepatitis B and tuberculosis. The authors noted that at times these rates exceeded the rates of other minority groups in the United States.

APIA Nurse Workforce

According to the U.S. Dept. of Health and Human Services (1994), there is a total of 76,000 licensed Asian and Pacific Islander registered nurses or 3.4 percent of the total registered nurse population in the United States. The data on the supply of registered nurses also reveals the following characteristics regarding APIA nurses:

- a majority of the registered nurses are foreigners trained rather than graduates of U.S. nursing programs,
- a majority are baccalaureate prepared and received this education in a foreign country,
- 85 percent are employed in hospitals, and
- 84 percent work full-time.

The National League for Nursing (NLN) (1994) reports no change for Asian American admissions into nursing programs from 1990 to 1993. The NLN reported that of the 41,290 students enrolled in baccalaureate nursing programs in the U.S. from 1992–1993, 1,664 (4.0 percent) were identified as Asians. This lack of change is attributed to the small effort targeting Asians in nursing recruitment (Kuramoto and Louie 1996). Also, the percentage of Asians graduating from baccalaureate programs were 4.0 percent (1990–91), 3.5 percent (1991–92) and 3.8 percent (1992–93). Attrition rates of .9 percent to .4 percent for Asians were reported in these programs.

The American Association of Colleges of Nursing (AACN) (1995) reports that enrollment of basic nursing students in bachelors' degree programs continued to increase by 2.6 percent during the 1994–1995 year. The proportion of students from racial/ethnic minority groups remained stable with 16.9 percent of basic baccalaureate students and 11.4 percent who were masters' students. The AACN reports rates which show a slight increase in the number of Asians enrolled from 1993–94 to 1994–95: 4.2 percent to 4.6 percent in generic baccalaureates, 2.0 percent to 2.1 percent in RN baccalaureates and 3.1 percent to 3.2 percent in masters' programs. They also report that the percentage of graduation for Asians for 1993 is 3.4 percent and 1994 3.5 percent in generic baccalaureate programs and 2.0 percent and 2.4 percent in RN baccalaureate programs. Attrition rates of .8 percent to 1.1 percent in generic baccalaureate programs were also reported.

Financial Incentives (Cost and Quality)

The focus on culturally competent care is related to the quality of services provided by registered nurses. Since a majority of APIA nurses are bicultural and bilingual, it is imperative that these nurses are targeted and recruited into nursing programs particularly where large APIA populations are found. In addition to identifying the various APIA subgroups, these nurses would be able to understand and assist clients in managing their own health care. Preparation of APIA bicultural and bilingual professional nurses educated from nursing programs in the US also would have the understanding of the dominant Western view of health and illness.

Generally APIA nurses would return or stay employed in the community in which they have families. This would contribute to the need for APIA nurses in urban areas such as New York, Chicago, San Francisco and Los Angeles. In the surveys of APIA nurses, this group has the highest rate of full-time employment than any other group of registered nurses.

Perceptions of Nursing as a Career

Nursing as a career choice is viewed as a positive occupation by Asian and Pacific Islanders. There are varying reasons which make this profession attractive. Deciding to enter a nursing program continues to be gender related, specifically for women. Young women are encouraged to enter nursing because these skills are what many women are taught in the families, e.g., nurturing roles. The field is also seen as providing a service to others which would be in consonant with the beliefs of giving and caring for others. Others feel that the nursing field is valued because of the status it provides to the family particularly if the daughter is the first in the family to enroll in college. Nurses are viewed as an authority figures who possess the knowledge to care for the sick. Nursing is chosen because it is a university-based career and education in general is valued. In the U.S., the financial rewards are greater for women in nursing than in other careers.

Recruitment

Recruitment of Asian and Pacific Islander students into nursing requires input from several departments in the college. This includes admissions, students' services, academic support, public relations and members of the nursing department. It is generally known that there has not been a major focus in recruiting Asian and Pacific Islanders due to the myth of over representation.

First and foremost, the regions and areas where the college generally recruits must be identified and resources appropriated. The nursing program must prioritize whether targeting this population would enrich the diversity of the students and whether these students upon graduation would be provide the cultural competence necessary to care for clients.

Specific strategies in targeting Asian and Pacific Islanders include:

- Identifying specific high schools where Asian students are enrolled,
- Identifying neighborhoods where Asian families reside,
- Approaching churches, associations and community groups where Asian families are members,
- Contacting community health and nursing groups for prospective students,
- Advertising information in Asian newspapers, professional health journals, ethnic nursing organizations and chapters, and the media.

Specific informational materials (brochures, diskettes, Internet, bulletins boards) should include the following:

- Provide attractive brochures depicting Asian and Pacific Islander nurses from diverse backgrounds, and
- Provision of scholarships and incentives for enrollment in the nursing program.

After students have applied to the program, conduct initial screening interviews to explain the program and requirements. Invite the student and family members to the college to speak to the faculty and see the facilities.

Retention

Retention of Asian and Pacific Islander students is based upon several factors, academic, financial, and social. Academic support includes resources such as writing, assistance in the sciences, etc. Social support includes nonacademic related services which would make the student feel a sense of belonging to the college. Social supports include other Asian and Pacific Islander students on campus, an acknowledgment of the important holidays, etc.

Specific retention strategies include:

- Providing Asian mentors and role models by contacting alumni, and Asian nurses groups or chapters in the local area; and
- Teaching the faculty to be alert to students who experience academic difficulty. Asian students generally are uncomfortable in asking for help although they may need it.
- It is important to note that the student's level of acculturation in the United States is a consideration for APIA students. The less time the family is in the United States, the more traditional the behaviors toward authority and learning styles. There are fourth and fifth generation APIAs and these students are generally acculurated in Western society and generally would view these specific strategies as demeaning and stereotyping Asian and Pacific Islanders.

As the surveys noted earlier, there is attrition among APIAs in nursing programs. There is little documented as to the reasons for this. I surmise that the nonacademic issues such as acculturation, understanding how to survive in college, financial, and family obligations would impact upon the academic ability of these students. There generally is a strong emphasis on educational achievement between first and second generation families and the high value of not asking for assistance. The concept of "saving face" is important for the individual. The achievements and failures of students are reflected upon the family. Therefore, there is pressure to perform well in their academic studies. Students' successes in the Western culture are generally seen as belonging to the individual. Faculty and counselors need to understand this difference during academic advisement with APIA students.

Graduation

Upon graduation and completion of the registered nurse licensing examination, it is important to mentor the graduate nurse into the nursing profession. It would be ideal for the graduate to have participated in student nurses' organizations on campus. This may not be true with some APIA students because of the need to achieve in their studies. Extracurricular activities are not encouraged in traditional families. Belonging to ones professional nursing association offers various incentives for these nurses. These include reduced membership fees for the first year, volunteering in annual state nurses convention, becoming a buddy with an experienced nurse and having members of ethnic nursing organizations or chapters speak to nursing students before graduation.

Continued mentoring of these graduates by nurses in leadership positions is important. Ethnic nurses, particularly APIA nurses, need to have role models that encourage them to participate in professional nursing issues.

Recommendations

In order to successfully recruit and increase the number of APIA students into nursing programs, several recommendations are suggested. The various APIA subgroups must be identified and appropriate recruitment strategies planned. The commitment to focus on increased enrollment of these diverse groups must be made by the nursing faculty as well as the other departments in the institution. A clear recruitment and marketing plan need to include alumni of the program and other members of the ethnic community. The members can assist in recruitment of students and their families. The faculty or recruiter must be visible in the community, particularly where health programs are offered.

The marketing plan needs to include data specifically related to the need for bicultural and bilingual nurses. Also included should be the documented health status of Pacific Islanders, Asian American immigrants and refugees in the community. Many of the local or state agencies categorize APIA health data under the ethnic classification of "Other." Unfortunately, this continues to be the common practice in regions where there are a small number of APIA families. If this is the case, efforts need to be made to ascertain information from APIA clients regarding their perception of health needs and services.

The specific recruitment strategies include identifying potential APIA students for nursing programs as well as sources for advertisements. Another incentive for recruitment of students is to provide financial assistance in terms of scholarships and loans for tuition and/or board. Traditional APIA families generally do not have the financial resources to support a student in a four-year program.

These financial incentives also pertain to the federal initiatives to provide funding to nursing programs. The Bureau of Health Professions needs to prioritize funding for programs that serve predominantly Asian or Pacific Islander populations in the United States and its territories. The goal is to prepare grants assistance for projects designed to increase nursing education opportunities for students from disadvantaged backgrounds. It was reported by the Division of Nursing in the fiscal year of 1995 that the Nursing Education Opportunities for Individuals from Disadvantaged Backgrounds supported seven grants totaling $1,214,405 which focused on the special initiatives for Africans Americans and Hispanics. The competitive award is based upon the ability of the project directors to write grants. Institutions and APIA nurses in the Pacific Islands generally do not have the funds to hire a consultant nor the network because of the distance between islands and the lack of advanced educational preparation of these nurses.

Enrollment, retention and graduation strategies generally do not differ greatly from other ethnic minority students in the U.S. except to recognize that the model minority stereotype of APIA students is a myth. There are many APIA students who are graduating in the top one percent of their high schools and enrolling in Ivy league colleges. These students probably will not be the ones who enter nursing programs. In addition, APIA students may leave nursing programs due to non-academic issues previously discussed.

Increasing the recruitment, retention and graduation of Asian and Pacific Islander students, a majority who are bicultural and bilingual, would provide the culturally competent care to clients and families of specific subgroups of Asian and Pacific Islanders.

Audrey Koertvelyessy, MSN, RN, PNP

The Status of Nursing Among Minority Populations: Focus on the American Indian/Alaskan Natives

There are at least 577 American Indian/Alaskan Native tribes that are currently recognized by the federal government. Each of these tribes has the status of a sovereign nation vis-a-vis the government of the United States of America. Cumulatively, these tribes comprise approximately 2.2 million individuals who are spread out across both urban as well as reservation areas. It is estimated that approximately 50 percent of Indians live in urban areas. In general, the Indian population is younger than the non-Indian population in the United States (USDHHS1996). According to the 1990 Census, Indians have lower incomes than the general population. In 1989, Indians residing on the current reservation states had a median household income of $19,886 compared with $30,056 for the non-Indian population. During this time period, 31.6 percent of Indians lived below the poverty level in contrast to 13.1 percent of the non-Indian population. Beyond these aggregate data, each of the American Indian/Alaskan Native tribes and communities is best characterized as highly individualized. There is great heterogeneity that exists among the tribes. Each tribe has its own language, material culture, health belief system and practices, economy, political system, etc. While there may be similarities among some tribes that comprise a nation state or confederacy level form of government, for example, mutual intelligibility in languages among the Iroquois tribes, there is less homogeneity that actually exists among the individual tribes.

For the American Indian/Alaskan Native nurses, generally less is known than for other minorities. Data from the 1992 and 1996 National Sample Survey of Nurses (USDHHS 1992 and 1996) conducted by the Division of Nursing, Bureau of Health Professions, Health Resources and Services Administration indicates that the total number of American Indian/ Alaskan Native nurses is 9,988. These numbers are so small that further analysis is seldom conducted beyond merely calculating the overall percent of the group as a total of the minority nurses in the nation. The only survey of the American Indian/Alaskan Native nurse population was conducted by the former American Indian Alaskan Native Nurses Association during the 1970s. That survey remains the most comprehensive source of data to date. However, it is no longer representative due to the increases in numbers, although small, and the subsequent changes in the educational preparation of Indian nurses. The newly reorganized National Alaskan Native American Indian Nurses Association has expressed recent interest in conducting a survey of students and registered nurses who are American Indian or Alaskan Native to obtain a more accurate and current profile. This association also has an expressed goal of increasing the number of students enrolled and graduating from schools of nursing.

The profession of nursing is still viewed as a valued profession to pursue among the American Indian/Alaskan Native populations. While there are additional opportunities to pursue other careers, such as law, medicine, pharmacy, etc., nursing continues to be a popular choice among the youth in this minority population. This may be related to the time required to complete the educational program as well as the availability of employment upon completion. Nursing still offers both of these advantages, which are considered positive assets by the students

The initial level of educational preparation most frequently engaged in by the American Indian/Alaskan Native student remains the associate degree level. The choice of a school close to the student's home which is usually on or near the reservation remains the first choice for most. This is largely due to the presence of the family and community. The family structure is often an extended family which includes many family members with many responsibilities and obligations for students while in school. The students will have obligations that include bringing their families with them to the school setting and/or traveling home to the reservation to tend to family obligations. A single parent family with the student serving as the sole parent is common. While the associate degree offers introductory level preparation, American Indian/Alaskan Native students tend not to pursue further nursing education beyond this initial level. The desire to serve as a key support for the family coupled with the desire to serve the tribe are significant factors for Indian students. Educators should take this into account when both recruiting and planning a baccalaureate or higher degree nursing program.

Recruitment is only one-half of the equation, while retention, equally important, is the other half of the equation. Retention variables will be discussed in this section. Previous educational preparation obtained at the high school level may need strengthening, particularly in the math and science areas. It is important to provide tutorial services while the student is in school. Preparatory work to obtain needed study skills may be needed along with writing skills to survive the rigorous nursing curriculum demands. The need for a more active retention program that includes academic and social support is essential for students. Some who are involved have coined the term "intrusive monitoring" to describe the more active and aggressive monitoring needed by the American Indians students. Often the students are reluctant to admit or seek assistance with academic issues until they have failed in their course work and leave school altogether. Asking for assistance is likely to be viewed as a sign of weakness or failure and not as a sign of strength. At this point, further intervention is often too late. Maintaining close contact rather than waiting until the student fails and then never returns to the program is essential for retention of the these students.

Providing for an Indian presence on the campus or at the school site is equally important. This means planning for social activities, such as Pow-Wows. These activities are important to providing a cultural connection with the home base regardless of whether it is an urban or a reservation area. Role models are also extremely important to maintaining a strong identity during the important socialization process into nursing that occurs during the education program. Availability of mentors for support and guidance are equally important to the student's success. Clinical experience among American Indian individuals and families/communities should be encouraged and arranged for whenever possible.

The majority of the initiatives to encourage students into the health professions by way of recruitment, retention, and graduation activities are conducted by the Indian Health Service (IHS), a Federal agency whose mission is to raise the health care status of American Indians and Alaskan Natives to the highest possible level. Within this agency there is a Congressionally established scholarship program. The sole purpose of this unique scholarship program is to provide health professional scholarships to students from the Indian and Alaskan tribes and communities. This scholarship is highly competitive and the selection process utilized is a rigorous one. Although all health professional students compete for the scholarship directly from the agency, a preference is given to American Indian and Alaskan Native nursing students. In fact, It serves as the major source for supporting Indian nursing students while in school. The pre-professional scholarship phase allows a student to obtain the needed study skills and prerequisite courses while incurring no obligation. The professional scholarship phase allows a student to pursue the professional preparation with an obligation to complete a period of service with an American Indian or Alaskan Native health care program upon completion. There is a two-year service obligation incurred for every year of scholarship received. Service can be with any federal or tribal health care program serving Indians or Alaskan Natives. The scholarship itself covers tuition and other reasonable costs along with a monthly stipend. Funds are sent directly to the student and not to the school. Students seldom have to work while attending school when receiving this scholarship. More importantly, upon completion the students are likely to return to their home reservation to provide service and generally remain there for the rest of their professional careers. After all, for the most part, they are generally returning to serve their own families and neighbors.

Another important source of support is the Nursing Recruitment Program established within IHS. In 1988, legislation was obtained to establish a competitive grant program which awarded funds to schools of nursing and other eligible entities that recruited, retained, and graduated students who indicated a desire to provide health care to the American Indian and Alaskan Native populations. The program was initially funded and implemented in 1990. Preference is given to American Indian and Alaskan Native students. The amount available to each student in this scholarship program is the same as in the IHS scholarship program. However, in this case, the award is made directly to the school and the school has the responsibility of administering the scholarship program. Students apply directly to the school and compete at the school level for the scholarship. Two tribal community colleges and three university programs are currently being supported. In the case of one state supported school, a state with a high Indian population, the increase in numbers of students has been phenomenal. In 1990, this school had only approximately three to four Indian students in the undergraduate program and none in the graduate program. As of the fall of 1996, there were forty-three students in the undergraduate program and fifteen in the graduate program. Not only are the students increasing in numbers, but they are also graduating. Several of these students are now discussing continuing on to the doctoral level of study. However, these few schools represent the greatest concentration of Indian students throughout the Nation. If more schools were to increase their efforts, or to take the time to analyze a successful program and discover what needs to be done to realistically recruit and support Indian students, the percentage of Indian students among all enrolled students just might rise to above 1 percent.

One of the significant characteristics of these successful programs is the presence of American Indian staff involved in the program, albeit small in numbers. The importance of staff and mentors cannot be overemphasized. Those few Indians who serve as mentors and recruiters are both aware and sensitive to the needs of the students and have the knowledge of how to effectively enter into the Indian community for recruitment purposes. In addition, few educational programs have American Indian nursing faculty members. The total number of American Indian nursing faculty remains extremely low throughout the country. Further, not only are there few faculty, but the total number of American Indian faculty who are doctorally prepared is even lower. Reaching a critical mass of American Indian doctorally-prepared faculty remains a goal yet to be achieved. The presence of role models as faculty members is another additional feature of programs that are successful in retaining students in school. The need to recruit and promote American Indian faculty in schools of nursing is an essential strategy that must be pursued on a national level.

Most American Indian and Alaskan Natives nurses return to their home communities to work after graduation from nursing school. Even those who do not have a scholarship obligation tend to return to practice on the home reservation or urban area serving primarily American Indians and Alaskan Natives. While salaries may not be commensurate with salaries elsewhere, the recognition of the health care needs and the desire to be a part of improving the tribal health situation remains a paramount goal for these nursing graduates.

Lisa Cruz-Avalos, MSN, RN, CS

Hispanic Representation in Nursing

General Overview

"The views expressed in this article are the author's and do not reflect those of the U.S. Department of Health and Human Services."

Hispanics in this country are one of the fastest growing minority populations. It is imperative that the nursing profession, like other disciplines, is prepared to provide services which adequately meet the needs of this group. One of the most fundamental methods of assuring this population such service is to prepare an appropriate number of Hispanics in nursing. Not only does this have patient benefit, but non-Hispanic nurses in general stand to gain knowledge from their Hispanic counterparts at the professional level. However, the number of Hispanic nurses remains severely disproportionate to that of the overall Hispanic population in this country. According to the most current National Sample Survey of Registered Nurses, 1.6 percent of the nurses in this nation are of Hispanic background (1996). The fact that this reflects such insignificant levels of change from previous Sample Survey results (i.e., 1.4 percent in 1992) warrants serious consideration at federal, state, and local levels.

In 1990, there were approximately 22.4 million Hispanics in the United States, almost 9 percent of the nation's people (U.S. Bureau of the Census 1993). Further projections indicate that Hispanics may be 13 percent of the United States' population by the year 2010. Within the Hispanic population, subgroups have experienced distinct levels of population growth. The Mexican population in the U.S. nearly doubled between 1979 and 1980 and then again by 1990. Cuban and Puerto Rican groups grew at a rate at least four times that of the rest of the nation. Additionally, Central and South American immigrants grew dramatically during the last decade. Despite the current and anticipated growth of Hispanics in this country, data from the U.S. Bureau of Labor Statistics (1993) show that the overall representation among Hispanics in the health professions remains inconsistent with the proportion of Hispanics in the nation. Though the 1980s brought out some minor peak numbers of both Hispanic physicians and physician assistants, such progress, albeit minimal, was not observed in nursing. Currently, less than 2 percent of the registered nurse population in this country are of Hispanic background (USDHHS 1994).

Clearly, each Hispanic subgroup is distinct and offers characteristics which lead to the richness and variety of the whole. Because of the heterogeneity of the group, it is vital that inquiry into recruitment and retention strategies effective for Hispanics be examined for each subgroup. This requires recognition of the cultural and social needs of those from Cuban, Mexican, Puerto Rican and other Hispanic backgrounds. The geographical profile of Hispanics in this country also provides guidance in terms of planning and developing strategies which effectively target specific subgroups.

Though broad, data collected at national levels address some of the issues and provide a preliminary framework to guide further work in the recruitment, retention, and graduation of Hispanic nurses. For example, certain census data is reflective of the societal issues which contribute indirectly to the overall low representation of Hispanic in nursing. Low income and poor educational environments serve as major barriers for the entrance of many Hispanics into programs of nursing. Thus, effective strategies for the recruitment and retention of Hispanics must include strategies of preparation at educational levels at or before secondary levels of education to move prospective nurses into competitive positions for program entry. Programs which merely target the group in the months just prior to college entry are "too little, too late" to impact the pool of Hispanic individuals entering nursing programs. Similarly, serious recruitment efforts should include financial and academic support options for individuals to explore before and after admission into nursing programs.

To date, issues of recruitment and retention of Hispanics into nursing have received limited focus. Most studies in the area lack depth and rigor. Additionally, programs which focus on strategies for recruitment, retention, or both, lack comprehensive evaluation plans which could build on the limited knowledge base currently available. These issues must provide the foundation for all future work aimed at improving the representation of Hispanics in nursing.

While research in the area of Hispanic health is beginning to draw more attention, the lack of inquiry related to the development of a representative Hispanic nursing workforce is phenomenal. For example, literature describing the effect of recruitment and retention efforts currently or traditionally utilized to improve Hispanic nursing representation is often anecdotal and lacks valid evaluation components.

Current Practice Levels and Workplace Settings of Hispanic Nurses

According to the 1992 National Sample Survey of Registered Nurses, Hispanic nurses were more likely to have received their basic nursing education in associate degree programs than other groups (USDHHS 1994). Approximately 46 percent of Hispanic nurses entered nursing at the associate degree level. On the other hand, the proportion of Hispanic nurses who had their basic nursing education in a baccalaureate program did not differ significantly from the proportion of White nurses according to the same survey. It is important to note that data collected for the survey occurred during a period marked by the popularity of associate degree programs with associate degree nursing graduates surpassing both their diploma and baccalaureate prepared counterparts. As the results of the subsequent surveys are reported, it will be interesting to see how the current "push" for baccalaureate prepared nurses to meet the changing health care needs of our nation will impact the basic nursing preparation of Hispanics.

In terms of advanced practice, approximately 6 percent of the Hispanic nurse population have a masters or doctoral degree (USDHHS 1994). Like the Hispanic nurse population prepared at the baccalaureate level, this number does not differ significantly from that of White nurses. This indicates a fairly decent pipeline for advance practice nurses from the baccalaureate prepared Hispanic graduates and serves as an important point when considering the need for Hispanic nurse leadership in all areas of the profession. Irrespective of level of preparation, Hispanic nurses contribute strongly to the nurse workforce. In fact, over 90 percent of the Hispanic nurse group are employed in nursing positions.

Data collected on Hispanic physicians indicate a likelihood to serve in areas with high numbers of Hispanics as well as other underserved patient groups (Fox 1996). Although such findings have been generalized to include Hispanic nurses, comprehensive studies which analyze the workplace trends of Hispanic nurses are limited. It is known that 72 percent of employed Hispanic nurses work in hospitals, a figure higher than that for all nurses in general (USDHHS 1994). Most Hispanic nurses working in hospitals serve at the staff level which is consistent with the majority of this group's level of nursing preparation. Hispanics participating in faculty positions contributed to less than 1 percent of the nation's nursing faculty which is not unexpected considering the limited pool available for academic positions (NLN 1992). In 1992, over 80 percent of the Hispanic nurse population practiced in metropolitan settings which mirrors U.S. Census information demonstrating a 90 percent metropolitan based population among Hispanics (USDHHS 1994; U.S. Bureau of the Census 1993).

The Selection of Nursing as a Career

There is a general belief that Hispanics in this country view nursing to be a subservient role, consistent with the nursing role described in many Latin countries. However, investigative studies in the U.S. focusing on this topic are limited in the nursing literature. Those which have focused on public perception of nursing and included Hispanics in sample populations generally report findings at aggregate levels. In one particular study, over 700 high school students were surveyed to examine their opinions on nursing (Grossman and Northrop 1993). The findings, which included a sample population existing of 25 percent Hispanics, revealed that positive perceptions of nursing focus around caring for people and assisting them to lead healthy lives (Grossman, Arnold, Sullivan, Cameron, and Munro 1989). Furthermore, student perception's of nursing are reportedly influenced by parents, peers and persons in advisory roles. In a similar study which reported findings specific to female Hispanic students at the secondary level, working in safe places, positive financial rewards, and being respected and appreciated were viewed as important nursing characteristics (Reiskin and Haussler 1994). Generally however, nursing has not been perceived as a role with opportunities to provide leadership and independent thinking which is consistent with the subservient role of nurses in Latin countries as noted above.

For Hispanics, the selection of "other careers" versus nursing is not *the* central issue. The more critical and underlying issue is the fact that almost 75 percent of Hispanic high school students are enrolled in nonacademic tracks, thereby severely decreasing the number of those adequately prepared to apply for nursing school entry (National Center for Education Statistics 1995). This tied in with an overall high school drop out rate of 35 percent among Hispanics leads to the more obvious and serious problem; a limited pool of prospective nursing students. This problem is traced farther as significant gaps are revealed between Hispanics and Whites in reading, mathematics and science beginning as early as nine years of age (U.S. Department of Education 1995). In the face of educational inequities among Hispanics, it is worth noting that standardized test scores which have been consistently problematic for this group are the most heavily weighted criteria for entrance into many nursing programs. The fact that lower achievement in education has been shown to be directly correlated to such factors as socioeconomic status further complicates this scenario.

Important Variables for Hispanics Related to Recruitment, Retention and Graduation in Nursing

In addition to issues around the inadequate preparation of Hispanics for entrance into nursing programs, financial barriers are significant for this group. Currently, 40 percent of all Hispanic children live in poverty, the highest for all minority groups (DHHS 1995). Hispanics who do enter nursing programs, are inherently faced with a nursing institution which lacks elements important for the inclusion of Hispanics and other ethnic populations in the system. Such elements include an appropriate level of cultural sensitivity in the curriculum, access to ethnic nursing organizations that are based on a sound framework and that are recognized as important within the institution, and adequate mentors who are both willing and capable to recognize the richness that Hispanics bring to an institution and the nursing profession overall. According to Ruybal, social support strongly influences the successful participation and outcome of educational attainment of Hispanic nurses (Ruybal 1996). Furthermore, key elements to enhancing the student nurse experience for Hispanics and other underrepresented groups must be seen as more than just additions but as integral parts of the institution's mission.

Any discussion around health care access, service and delivery for Hispanics must include a description of the population of which we are speaking. Among the overall Hispanic population there are certain characteristics which are "shared." For example, language is a very important hallmark of culture and the Spanish language provides a sense of unity among subgroups. Other common cultural characteristics are harder to define though familialism, cultivation of personal relationships and alliances, are a few more often described in the literature. However, it is well known that Hispanics are not a homogenous group. Differences in educational preparation, socioeconomic and certain health indicators differ widely among Hispanic subgroups. In addition, within each subgroup also exists generational differences. Such differences are crucial for the comprehensive study of factors important for the recruitment and retention of Hispanics in nursing.

Conclusion

Hispanic nurses bring many qualities that are essential for the development of a workforce capable of caring for all persons in this country. Consistent with the general characteristics of this population, the Hispanic nurse is younger than all others which is an important consideration in terms of work years and the overall "graying" of the nurse workforce. With over half of the nation's Hispanic population reporting Spanish as their primary language, the cultural and linguistic capabilities of this underrepresented group in nursing are a necessary attribute for assuring appropriate health care to those of Hispanic backgrounds. The time to address the pipeline of Hispanic nurses is now as the diversity of this country continues to evolve.

Conclusion

Reading the text on the minority groups discussed in this chapter, it is clear that there are differences among (as well as within) the groups. However, the issues, impediments, and solutions affecting recruitment into and retention of nurses of color in nursing are shared by all four groups. In addition, the problems of recruitment and retention are not only difficulties experienced by persons from the four racial and ethnic groups, rather these problems are adversely affecting adversely the entire nursing profession. Patients of color will soon comprise the majority of patients receiving health care provided at community levels. If nursing is to fulfill its mission of providing culturally competent and sensitive care to these patients, more attention and resources will have to be devoted to increasing the numbers of nurses of color at all educational levels in order to increase the numbers of well prepared nurses of color in the profession. This increase can only be achieved through dedicated commitment to creatively designed and aggressively implemented recruitment and retention efforts.

References

AAN Expert Panel Report. 1992. Culturally competent health care. *Nursing Outlook* 40(6): 277–283.

American Association of Colleges in Nursing (AACN). 1995. *1994–1995 Enrollment and gradations in baccalaureate and graduate programs in nursing.* Publication N. 94-95-1. Washington, DC: Author.

Andrew, M. 1992. Cultural perspectives on nursing in the 21st century. *Journal of Professional Nursing* 8(1): 7–15.

Aponte, H. 1994. *Bread and spirit: Therapy with the new poor: Diversity of race, culture, and values.* New York: W.W. Norton & Company.

Avery, B. 1992. The health status of Black Women. In *Health issues in the Black community,* edited by R. Braithwaite and S. Taylor. San Francisco: Jossey-Bass Publishers.

Barbee, E. 1993. Racism in U.S. nursing. *Medical Anthropology Quarterly* 7: 346–362.

Bessent, H. 1989. Postdoctoral leadership training for women of color. *Journal of Professional Nursing* 5: 279–282.

Billingsley, A. 1992. *Climbing jacob's ladder: The enduring legacy of African American families.* New York: Simon & Schuster.

Campbell, and N. Heider. 1986. Do nurses need mentors? *Image: Journal of Nursing Scholarships* 18: 110–113.

Campinha-Bacote, J., J. Yahle, and M. Langenkamp. 1996. The challenge of cultural diversity for nurse educators. *The Journal of Continuing Education in Nursing* 27(2): 59–64.

Carnegie, M.E. 1986. *The path we tread: Blacks in Nursing 1854–1984.* Philadelphia: J.P. Lippincott Co.

Chen, M.S., and B. Hawks. 1995. A debunking of the myth of the health of Asians and Pacific Islanders. *American Journal of Health Promotion* 8(4): 261–268.

Davis, L. 1992. Research directions of nurse researches for the 21st century: An African American perspective. *The Association of Black Nursing Faculty Journal* 3: 4–6.

DeWar, H. 1997. Look ahead to an America of All 'Minorities' in a few years. *The Philadelphia Inquirer,* May 11, A1, A10.

Division of Nursing. 1994. *Nursing initiatives to increase ethnic/racial minority representation.* Rockville, MD: U.S. Department of Health and Human Services.

Division of Nursing. 1996. *Advance Notes from the National Sample Survey of Registered Nurses.* Rockville, MD: Health Resources and Services Administration.

Elders, J. 1995. A critical issue: Health care reform. *Journal of National Black Nurses Association* 7(2): 3–9.

Felder, E. 1992. Meeting the challenge of mentoring African American nursing faculty: A strategy for professional development. *The Association of Black Nursing. Faculty Journal* 3: 86–88.

Fox, C. 1996. *Minority physicians fill critical need in California, UCSF study finds—implications for affirmative action.* [University of California, World Wide Web Page-Press Releases]. Available: . . .//www.sf.edu/campus/news/pressrel/pressrel.html#bes

Gopaul, and S. McNicol. 1993. *Working with West Indian families.* New York: The Guilford Press.

Greer, D. 1995. Minority underrepresentation in Nursing: Socioeconomic and political effect. *The ABN Journal* 6(2): 44–46.

Grossman, D.G., and C. Northrop. 1993. What high schools students think of a nursing career:A survey of Dade County senior high school students. *Journal of Nursing Education* 32(4): 157–162.

Grossman, D., L. Arnold, J. Sullivan, M. Cameron, and B. Munro. 1989. High school students perceptions of nursing as a career:A pilot study. *Journal of Nursing Education* 28: 18–21.

Guillermo, T. 1994. Are Asian/Pacific Islander Americans Underrepresented in Health Research? *Asian American and Pacific Islander Journal of Health* 2(4): 299–302.

Hacker, A. 1995. *Two nations: Black and White, separate, hostile, unequal.* New York: Ballantine Books.

Hale, C. 1992. A Demographic Profile of African American. In *Health issues in the Black community*, edited by R. Braithwaite and S. Taylor. San Francisco: Jossey-Bass Publishers.

Hine, D. 1989. *Black women in white: Racial conflicts and cooperation in the nursing profession, 1890–1950.* Bloomington & Indianapolis: Indiana University Press.

Jackson, Eileen. 1993. Whiting—Out differences: Why U.S. nursing research fails Black families. *Medical Anthropology Quarterly* 7(4): 363–385.

Kuramoto, A., and K.B. Louie. 1996. Asian/Pacific Islander American Nurses' Workforce: Issues and Challenges for the 21st Century. *Journal of Cultural Diversity* 3(4): 112–115.

Lin-Fu, J.S. 1993. Asian and Pacific Islander Americans: An overview of demographic characteristics and health care issues. *Asian American and Pacific Islander Journal of Health* 1: 20–36.

Lloyd, C. 1980. Life events and depression disorder reviewed, *Archives of General Psychiatry* 37: 520–548.

May, K., A. Meleis, and P. Winstea-Fry. 1982. Mentorship for scholarship: Opportunities and dilemmas. *Nursing Outlook* 30: 22–28.

Megel, M. 1985. New faculty in nursing: Socialization and the role of the mentors. *Journal of Nursing Education* 24: 303–306.

Myers, H. 1982. Research on the Afro-American Family: A Critical Review. In *The Afro-American family: Assessment, treatment, and research issues*, edited by B. Bass, G. Wyatt, and G. Powell. New York: Greene & Stratton.

National Center for Education Statistics. 1995. *Digest of educational statistics.* Washington, DC: U.S. Department of Education, Office of Educational Research and Improvement.

National League for Nursing, Division of Research. 1991. *Nursing data review.* New York: NLN Press.

National League for Nursing. 1994. *Nursing data source 1994. Vol. 1 Trends in contemporary nursing education.* Division of Research (Pub. No. 19-2642) New York: National League for Nursing Press.

Nursing Data Source. 1995. *Trends in Contemporary Nursing Education.* NLN Publication No. 19-6649. New York: National League for Nursing.

Outlaw, F. 1993. Stress and coping: The influence of racism on the cognitive appraisal processing of African Americans. *Issues in Mental Health Nursing* 14: 339–409.

Outlaw, F. 1995. Mentorship and Research Productivity after the Postdoctoral Fellowship: An African American Perspective. In *Successful Postdoctoral Research Training for African American Nurses,* edited by J. Fawcett & R. McCorkle. Washington, DC: American Academy of Nursing.

Phillips, J. 1995. Research for improving the health and well-being of the Black community: Implications for shaping a research agenda. *Journal of National Black Nurses Association* 7 (2): 21–28.

Porter, C., and A. Villarruel. 1993. Nursing research with African American and Hispanic people: A guideline for action. *Nursing Outlook* 41(2): 59–67.

Powell, D. 1992. The recruitment and retention of African American nurses: An analysis of current data. *Journal of National Black Nurses Association* 6(1): 3–12.

Reiskin, H., and S.C. Haussler. 1994. Multicultural students' perceptions of nursing as a career. *IMAGE: Journal of Nursing Scholarship* 26(1): 61–64.

Ruybal, S.E. 1996. Educational opportunities for Hispanic nursing: A community-based model. In *Hispanic voices, Hispanic health educators speak out,* edited by S. Torres. New York: NLN Press.

U.S. Bureau of the Census. 1993. *Current population reports: Hispanic Americans today* (Census Profile No. P23–183). Washington, DC: Government Printing Office.

U.S. Bureau of Labor Statistics. 1993. In secondary source, *Project 3000 by 2000: Health Partnerships Initiative.*

U.S. Department of Education. (1995, August). *The condition of education.* [US Department of Education Publications]. Available: . . ./www.ed.gov/pubs/CondOfEd95/ovw2html.

U.S. Department of Health and Human Services. (1996, September). *Hispanic Customer Service Demographics.* [Hispanic Demographics] Available: . . .//www.dhhs.gov/about/heo/hisp.html.

U.S. Department of Health and Human Services. Health Resources and Services Administrtion, Division of Nursing. 1992. *The registered nurse population 1992. Findings from the national sample survey of registered nurses.* Washington, DC: Government Printing Office.

U.S. Department of Health and Human Services (USDHHS). 1994. Health resources and services administration. *The registered nurse population. Findings from the national sample survey of registered nurses, March 1992.* Washington, DC: U.S. Department of Health and Human Services.

U.S. Department of Health and Human Services. Health Resources and Services Administration, Division of Nursing. 1997. *The registered nurse population 1996. Findings from the national sample survey of registered nurses.* Washington, DC: Government Printing Office.

U.S. Department of Health and Human Services. Indian Health Service. 1996. *Trends in Indian health, 1996.* Washington, DC: Government Printing Office.

Williams, R., and R. Blackburn. 1988. Mentoring and junior faculty productivity. *Journal of Nursing Education* 27: 204–209.

7

Recruitment, Retention and Graduation of Minority Nurses: Philosophical Considerations

Lucius Outlaw, PhD

Efforts to recruit persons of minority racial and ethnic groups into college and university nursing programs, to retain them in ways and on terms that allow and encourage them to flourish—not just survive, and to have them graduate and move on to successful careers as caregivers and contributors to nursing are complex, related endeavors of long-term social engineering. They require particular agendas and resources defined and coordinated by a mission-setting agenda to which all parties involved must be firmly committed.

Reaching consensus regarding this mission and agenda, and on the efforts by which to fulfill them, is not difficult for many persons when expressed in ways that capture the spirit and terms of what are widely regarded as the founding ideals and guiding principles of the American Republic, namely, that such efforts be "color blind." That is, that they be devoted to providing equal access to all opportunities for development and achievement to all individuals, "without regard to race, creed, color, sex, or national origin," who are capable and willing to take advantage of the opportunities. It is much more difficult, however, to reach consensus, whether within organizations, institutions, or across the nation generally, regarding the appropriate means by which to provide opportunities—on what terms, to whom, and to what ends—when doing so involves targeting efforts on particular racial and ethnic groups. More challenging still is the vexing question whether it is ever appropriate not just to provide access to opportunities, but to work to ensure outcomes: to go beyond efforts to ensure that persons in minority racial and ethnic groups have full knowledge of and fair access to opportunities for nursing education, and on to efforts to ensure that once they have entered educational programs, they continue and graduate.

For many persons in the United States of America, targeting persons of color as recipients of opportunities *because they are persons of color* is not just unfair to potential partakers of the opportunities who are not "of color," but unjust because the targeting violates constitutional prohibitions against making discriminating judgments on the basis of race, creed, color, and sex (or physical ability) in the distribution of rewards and sanctions. With increasing frequency, a majority of the Justices on the United States Supreme Court, in reaching decisions on cases involving these matters, are ruling that such judgments are unconstitutional.

Many other persons (less than a majority of Americans according to several polls), for a variety of reasons, disagree. A common belief among these persons is that, in view of the long history of *invidious*[1] racial and ethnic discriminations directed against peoples of color by persons of various ethnic groups and nationalities deriving from Europe who became racially unified in America as members of a superior "white" race, the achievement of just distribution of opportunities cannot be achieved through efforts blind to race and ethnicity even though invidious racial discrimination and segregation are no longer part of the laws of the land. To the contrary, laws prohibiting such practices are part of legal and administrative structures and moral codes throughout the nation. Rather, many believe, the inertia of commitments to privileges of white superiority as well as invidious judgments of peoples of color are nonetheless well institutionalized throughout American society after nearly three centuries and continue to affect the distributions of rewards and sanctions, including distributions of educational opportunities. Moreover, the centuries of science and church-sanctioned institutionalized invidious discrimination in support of white racial superiority also had negative impacts on the self-understandings and self-identifications of many people of color. One consequence, in numerous cases, has been

---

[1]It is impossible to go about daily life without routinely making discriminating judgments of numerous kinds, judgments in which we make distinctions, differentiate, distinguish between and among and valorize persons, objects, situations. However, much to our detriment, it is common practice today to regard any and all instances of "discrimination" as inappropriate, no matter what the o intention, when judging persons on the basis of race or ethnicity: discriminating *for* black and other folks of color because of their race is thought by many to be the same as discriminating *against* them because of their race. If discrimination is wrong in the latter case because it is predicated on racial distinctions, then it is wrong in cases of the former kind for the same reasons. Racial discrimination, it is argued, is racial discrimination; and racial discrimination is wrong. Discrimination is wrong.

This line of argument proceeds by a logic of reduction to simplicity carried to absurdity. The full reality of life is infused with complexity and nuance *requiring* us to make judgments of distinction, *requiring* us to discriminate—sometimes negatively, sometimes positively. What we must have when such judgments involve questions of social justice— that is, are judgments that involve distributions of opportunities, rewards and sanctions— are norms by which to determine whether discriminating judgments (say a policy that invokes or guides the making of such judgments) are or are not appropriate: whether or not the discriminating judgment furthers social justice and humanistic regard for other human beings. Discriminating judgments that fail these tests I regard as "invidious" and will so identify them throughout this essay. I hope others will be persuaded of the desperate need to do likewise in order to return some measure of indispensable common sense, sanity and nuance to our efforts to deal justly with the nuances and complexities of racial and ethnic pluralism.

the cultivation of unnecessarily and inappropriately lowered self-expectations on the part of many persons of color (and, frequently, low expectations of them by others), another the under-exploitation of educational opportunities in certain fields and professions.

Centuries of practices favoring white people and disfavoring people of color, rationalized by beliefs in white racial superiority and the inferiority of colored races, have facilitated the continuing racially and ethnically skewed accumulation and perpetuation of material, financial and cultural capital—including educational opportunities and achievements—by, within, and among social groupings of "white" people in gross disproportion to accumulations by peoples of color. These accumulations cannot be justified as having been achieved only by satisfying color-blind principles of equality of opportunity. The principles and rules of justice in America were racialized at the nation's founding, continued in effect well into the twentieth century, and served throughout to deny the opportunities and benefits of citizenship to virtually all persons not male and white. Rogers M. Smith has calculated that "[f]or over 80 percent of U.S. history, its laws declared most of the world's population to be ineligible for full American citizenship solely because of their race, original nationality, or gender. For at least two-thirds of American history, the majority of the domestic adult population was also ineligible for full citizenship for the same reasons" (Smith 1993, 549).

The legacy of America's history continues to condition life in this country via the inertia of culturally-reproduced invidious racial and ethnic prejudices and institutionalized practices, as well as the patterning of career aspirations within the subcultures of various racial and ethnic groups of people of color that result in comparative disproportionate numbers of such persons choosing careers in health care, nursing in particular. In the context of this history, there are ample grounds on which to be persuaded that concern to fulfill the requirements of justice by extending opportunity to all persons capable and willing to exploit educational opportunities. This requires focusing affirmative efforts on persons among racial and ethnic populations that heretofore have been the targets of invidious discrimination or otherwise have been less forthcoming comparatively in choosing nursing as a career. Efforts must be focused on taking appropriate steps to recruit, retain and graduate persons of color from programs devoted to producing successive generations of highly-educated and well-prepared professionals, nursing caregivers, researchers and scholars among them.

Not all persons will be so persuaded, even though there are numerous persons, organizations, and schools of nursing dedicated (some more than others) to just such efforts. For many persons, a majority of the Justices on the Supreme Court among them, the principles of justice—grounded in the founding principles of the nation-state as set forth in the Declaration of Independence and the Constitution, its Bill of Rights and subsequent amendments—are meant to be applied to *individuals* only, and then without regard to their race or ethnicity (or their religious creed, sex or gender). For these persons the nation's founding political principles constitute its core creed. Adherence to this creed is taken to be definitive of what it means to be an "American": that is, American identity is defined ideologically or politically (that is, by adherence to certain principles said to apply to all persons universally), not by race, ethnicity, language, or religion (cf. Smith 1988, 225ff).

Few, if any, persons who hold this view would deny the history of invidious racial and ethnic discriminations in this country, though some (hopefully few) might well harbor sentiments and engage in practices that most persons would denounce as racist or inappropriately prejudiced against persons of particular ethnic groups. Rather, it is likely that such persons, because of this history, would be most emphatic in insisting that we move, once and for all, to full compliance with the principles requiring color-blind administering of justice in the distribution of opportunities, educational and otherwise. And they would be very likely to insist on recognition of and adherence to another important element in the American creed: that individual citizens, in enjoying the blessings of liberty, among them the exploitation of opportunity, must do so as autonomous adults acting responsibly. That is, once equality of opportunity has been made available to all able and willing, it is the responsibility of individual persons to make the best of opportunities and to either fail or succeed *on their own*, without special assistance designed to ensure that they succeed.

This creedal ideal has enjoyed a vigorous history as a purported norm and regulative ideal and, in the process, has become well ensconced as a bedrock element in contemporary American political ideologies across virtually all racial and ethnic groups. But just how historically foundational is this ideal as an element among America's creedal beliefs? And to whatever extent it has functioned as a guiding ideal for many, how and why did efforts develop and become widely applied that have been devoted to securing opportunities for persons of color, and to trying to ensure their success in exploiting opportunities? In answering these questions we may have the clarity of purpose and assured conviction needed to rededicate efforts and resources to the recruitment, retention and graduation of nurses of color given the sentiments of a majority of Americans that special, "affirmative action" efforts in behalf of persons of color are inappropriate and unjust.

A long view back across America's history to the nation's founding should prove instructive. A particularly informative view, one that also provided an assessment that is helpful to this discussion, was provided by Alexis de Tocqueville in his *Democracy in America* (Tocqueville 1835 [1990]). Tocqueville, a brilliant young Frenchman traveling through the then forming American republic to assess the democratic project, was especially insightful and articulate in seeing the particular character of the new nation as being derived from what he termed "the national character" ("the prejudices, the habits, the ruling passions. . .") of its founding people:

> The growth of nations presents something analogous to
> this; they all bear some marks of their origin. The circum-

stances that accompanied their birth and contributed to their development affected the whole term of their being . . . At the period when the peoples of Europe landed in the New World, their national characteristics were already completely formed; each of them had a physiognomy of its own; and they had already attained that stage of civilization at which men are led to study themselves, they have transmitted to us a faithful picture of their opinions, their manners, and their laws . . . If we carefully examine the social and political state of America, after having studied its history, we shall remain perfectly convinced that not an opinion, not a custom, not a law, I may even say not an event is upon record which the origin of that people will not explain. (Tocqueville 1835 [1990], Vol. I, 26–28)

In Tocqueville's judgment, the national character out of which the particularly American version of a democratic nation-state was being formed was that of Anglo-Saxons, the national character being formed an Anglo-American civilization defined primarily by two distinct elements: the spirit of religion and the spirit of liberty (Tocqueville 1835 [1990], Vol. I, 43).

However, the nation-forming and character-forming civilizational project was complicated, in Tocqueville's judgment, by the cohabitation on the same land of what he (as did many others) regarded as three "naturally distinct" races: the European, the Negro and the Indian. Regarding these three races, "[a]lmost insurmountable barriers had been raised between them by education and law, as well as by their origin and outward characteristics; but fortune has brought them together on the same soil, where, although they are mixed, they do not amalgamate, and each race fulfills its destiny apart" (Tocqueville 1835 [1990], Vol. I, 332). How, Tocqueville pondered, would the project of forming a democratic nation proceed to fulfillment given the complications involving three incompatible races?

In the case of Indians, Tocqueville thought the outcome clear and inevitable: "I believe that the Indian nations of North America are doomed to perish, and that whenever the Europeans shall be established on the shores of the Pacific Ocean, that race of men will have ceased to exist" (Tocqueville 1835 [1990], Vol. I, 342). Either Indians would become equals of Europeans on the latters' terms or be destroyed. As the Indians, in Tocqueville's estimation, were too proud and haughty to submit to being civilized by Europeans, they would, consequently, be eliminated through genocide.

The relations between Europeans and Negroes were more complicated still: "the destiny of the Negroes is in some measure interwoven with that of the Europeans. These two races are fastened to each other without intermingling; and they are alike unable to separate entirely or to combine. The most formidable of all the ills that threaten the future of the Union arises from the presence of a black population upon its territory"

(Tocqueville 1835 [1990], Vol. I, 356). And why was the presence of Negroes in America, due to what he regarded as the "calamity" of slavery "restricted to one of the races of mankind" (Tocqueville 1835 [1990], Vol. I, 357), such a 'formidable ill'? Because he could see no way to resolve the calamity and its consequences: there were too many Negroes to be relocated to Africa; the two races, given their natural distinctivenesses, were unassimilable. Worse, there was a "fatal" development in American racialized slavery: "the abstract and transient fact of slavery is fatally united with the physical and permanent fact of color . . . the Negro transmits the eternal mark of his ignominy to all his descendants; and although the law may abolish slavery, God alone can obliterate the traces of its existence" (Tocqueville 1835 [1990], Vol. I, 357–358). Negroes' color became, says Tocqueville, a "visible and indelible sign" of ignominy that, even with the abolishment of slavery, would persist as an object of prejudice, along with the prejudice of the master and the prejudice of the race, that would have to be contended with, prejudices that would be difficult to attack and even more difficult to conquer. Color would always be a visible sign and symbol in which to invest the prejudices.

Tocqueville's prescient nineteenth century projections have, of course, been borne out, as has W.E.B. Du Bois's, that the problem of the twentieth century would be problems of 'the color line'. But confirmation of Tocqueville's predictions is not the point of this excursion. Nor is it to belabor the recognition that racism in various forms was part and parcel of the founding of the American republic. Rather, it is to recover an understanding that takes full cognizance of the racial and ethnic complexities that affected the nation's founding and its subsequent development. Such an understanding will require an alteration of the sense of the importance and social efficacy of certain principles and ideals articulated at the founding, and others developed since, that, in large measure, have formed the Liberal Enlightenment tradition of defining the identity of an American citizen. Namely, that to be an *American* is to be a person who relinquishes all allegiances to Old World national or tribal genealogical-class structured communities, their prejudices and defining ways of life, to become, instead, a self-made person of a Modern New World community defined by political principles and ideals that apply universally to all persons with the same rights who are essentially equal and whose remaining Old World commitments and sentiments are to be relegated to the realm of private, non-public life.

What Tocqueville sees is not a nation being formed according to this agenda alone, but one quite explicitly having to confront and resolve realities of interracial complexities and profound conflicts that threatened the success of the civilizational, nation-forming project. One of the strategies adopted relied on articulate accounts of racial differences provided by many of the most respected natural philosophers and statesmen of the day including, for example, Thomas Jefferson. In these accounts humans were seen as distributed around the earth in large, sometimes widely dispersed and diverse yet distinct population groups each of which was thought nonetheless to share a sufficient number of attributes as to be naturally determined by interrelated biological, social, and cultural characteristics including consequent dispositions, passions, aspirations, and capabilities. In Old World parlance, these population groups were (are) *nations* and *races* (the terms were often used interchangeably). And while there was hardly unanimity among those who bent their minds to identifying the different races or nations and explaining their differences, there did come to be a rather settled color-coded terminology for naming races and their members, a terminology that conflated all of the defining characteristics of each race into code-terms for the color of the skin of those individuals thought to be most representative of their race: red, white, brown, yellow, black (though combinations of skin color and other characteristics were needed to identify various groups not easily fitted into the five-color scheme).

Of course, the work of identifying, characterizing and categorizing social collectivities and populations was hardly a matter of disinterested natural philosophy (subsequently of the biological and social sciences), though this was the case for a number of those engaged in the efforts. Rather, they were endeavors of Europeans of a variety of national groups many of whom were also experiencing in various ways, even if not directly involved in, ventures of imperialism that brought them into conflictual contacts with other races and nations that were decidedly different the farther afield the Europeans traveled. For a variety of reasons and as part of the imperialist ventures, racial classification also became a moral, evaluational rank-ordering sorting of peoples along a hierarchical superior white—-red—yellow—brown—black inferior continuum that facilitated the conquest and management, for the benefit of "whites," of lands and resources of peoples "of color," and of such peoples themselves.

These were the tasks to be accomplished in creating the United States of America of and for self-selected Europeans intent on forming out of themselves a new civilization. For the men who served as architects of the new nation-civilization, the God-sanctified, self-evident founding principles and ideals were to apply to property (including African slave)-owning white men such as themselves without regard to distinguishing Old World characteristics (religion, social rank by birth, language). Equality and respect for God-given, inalienable rights were foundational aspects of citizenship these men understood themselves as sharing. In addition, they added to these commitments others that drew on various forms of republication thought that were devoted to the fashioning of institutions and practices that would "make collective self-governance in pursuit of a common good possible for the community as a whole" (Smith 1988, 231). And for the most part these men were satisfied that with proper guidance from them, other white males could develop in ways to fulfill the conditions for full citizenship.

However, the presence of indigenous "red-skinned" peoples occupying the land and thus blocking access to additional resources needed for the new civilizational project and its nation-state, peoples who had forms of life decidedly different from peoples with white skins, as well as the "calamity" of the evil of race-based enslavement of "black" Africans and their descendants to provide necessary labor, made for compelling needs for sharper distinctions of race and nationality, distinctions that defined who could and would be allowed to play what roles in nation building, and who would or could become a citizen of the new nation-state with the rights and privileges guaranteed by the successful revolutionary enlightened, liberal redefinition of the terms of citizenship. No less important was the need to maintain the biological and cultural distinctiveness, and decisive aspects of the very identities, of the descendants of Europeans as a "white" race. However, the situation was complicated by the desires of many Europeans and their descendants to maintain, albeit in altered form, their Old World national identities and cultures within or in addition to cultivating a racial identity as "white."

Efforts to satisfy all of these needs produced traditions of identity-formation and definitions of American citizenship that placed stress on what Rogers M. Smith (1988) refers to as "ethnocultural" identities. He has argued rather convincingly that what is widely regarded as the tradition of Enlightenment Liberalism, a definitive feature of which is emphasis on "equal concern and respect for the rights of every human being" (Smith 1988, 230), while certainly a decisive factor over the centuries in the forming of the American republic, has not been the only resource for civic identity-formation, not even the dominant one. In significant part because these commitments, while of revolutionary significance in helping to give form and direction to America as a paradigmatically modern nation-state, were seldom fully satisfying for most persons for whom they were intended since they required the abandonment of commitment to what, over centuries, had been thought to be the "natural authority" of membership in distinctive, inherited cultural communities that provided persons with senses of personal worth and meaningful collective life (Smith 1988, 230).

To satisfy these needs and concerns, stress on ethnocultural characteristics (ethnicity, place of birth), reinforced by scientific racialism and romantic cultural naturalism, would, under particular circumstances, be combined with liberal republicanism to make for a core of ideas definitive of ethnocultural Americanism—"nativism" in its extreme forms—that became well established criteria expressed in political rhetoric and scholarship for defining American civic identity:

> Arguments for such criteria were not made covertly, or in passion, or chiefly by the uneducated. They were defended openly, coolly, seriously, and at some length by the leading statesmen and intellectuals . . . who connected them with broader world-views within which such criteria seemed to make sense . . . While the theoretical elaborations came later, from the outset of the nation many Americans chiefly identified membership in their political community not with freedom for personal liberal callings or republican self-governance *per se*, but with a whole array of particular cultural origins and customs—with northern European, if not English, ancestry; with Christianity, especially dissenting Protestantism, and its message for the world; with the

white race; with patriarchal familial leadership and female domesticity; and with all the economic and social arrangements that came to be seen as the true, traditional 'American way of life'. (Smith 1988, 232–234)

Yet, Smith notes, there have been other, similar responses to many of the same needs that have given rise to ethnocultural Americanism, responses that have been tempered by Liberal traditions of respect for liberty and tolerance for divergent ethnocultural differences. These responses have given rise to what he regards as a much more cosmopolitan tradition of democratic cultural pluralism with less stress on achieving and maintaining a common national identity at the expense of nurturing identities growing out of ethnocultures. Increasingly over the last quarter-century, political and cultural life in America has been animated by commitments to various forms of (mostly) cosmopolitan cultural pluralism (distinguished from ideologies and movements devoted to racial and/or ethnic separatism) or, in today's prevailing terms, to various forms of "multiculturalism." So much so that Nathan Glazer, in surveying these developments in a recent book, has declared that "we are all multiculturalists now" (Glazer 1997) since the variety of quests to maintain racial and ethnic distinctiveness have displaced and all but completely discredited the goal of, as well as quests for, "assimilation" to a color-blind civic identity without racial or ethnic distinction, and displaced from predominance the still not totally discredited ethnocultural Americanism of white racial superiority.

While hardly celebrating the victory, Glazer, in an important and exemplary self-disclosing discussion in which he acknowledges having been wrong about the project of Americanization via assimilation which he had expected (and predicted) would work out for persons of African descent, the one non-European minority group even on the way to being *fully* integrated into the American republic, much the same as had been the case for European ethnics and more recent immigrants not of African descent, nonetheless accepts that the multiculturalists have "won": "we all accept a greater degree of attention to minorities and women and their role in American history and social studies and literature classes in schools. Those few who want to return American education to a period in which the various subcultures were ignored, and in which America was presented as the peak and end-product of civilization, cannot expect to make any progress in the schools" (Glazer 1997, 14).

And for good reason, for by the time Glazer has completed his review of the historical circumstances out of which cultural pluralism *cum* multiculturalism has come to prevail over assimilation as the governing agenda and guiding ideal of social movements and public policy, he has come to be fully persuaded that the project of assimilation involved serious moral lapses and failed miserably in the case of people of African descent:

> If we look back toward the nineteenth century from the perspective of the present, we can only be surprised at how unconcerned Americans were over the problem of

assimilation until the 1890s or so ... In almost all the
discussions of Americanization or assimilation until about
World War II, the participants have only Europeans in
mind. This is true whether they favored or opposed assimilation and Americanization efforts. Today, a reader of the
documents of the great Americanization drive of the second decade of this century will find no reference to blacks,
then as now our largest minority. It is as if the turmoil of
abolitionism, slavery, the Civil War, Reconstruction did not
exist. All concern was with the enormous numbers of
"new" immigrants from Eastern and Southern Europe, who
were different from the Europeans the nation had become
accustomed to. (Glazer 1997, 101–102)

The failures and lapses of the assimilation project involved more than
people of African descent. When combined with the intense, centuries-
long efforts of those committed to ascriptive ethnocultural "white" Americanism, peoples of color of almost all kinds were adversely affected as
well. Thus did the assimilationist Civil Rights Movement give rise to the
pluralist Black Power Movement that, for the most part, sought justice
and respect on cosmopolitan ethnocultural terms (there developed, as
well, various separatists currents). Both movements, however, inspired
and provided concrete experiences and lessons that informed subsequent movements for justice and respect for women and other peoples
of color. As Glazer observes in *We Are All Multiculturalists Now*, preva-
lent forms of these movements now find expression as quests for multiculturalism that have had some of their greatest impacts on and within
institutions devoted to education. Efforts devoted to recruiting, retaining,
and graduating persons of color in programs of nursing education are
but one example.

Are such efforts appropriate? Yes, both appropriate and necessary, politically and historically: these efforts are made necessary by a long history
of inappropriate attention to forming a unified nation out of persons
who comprise, and thus draw significant aspects of their identities and
senses of meaning and life-orientations from, racialized ethnocultural
groups and communities. They are appropriate for persons who,
throughout this nation's history, have continued to find unsatisfying
liberal and republican conceptions of civic identity void of ethnocultural
identity (Smith 1993, 558). In response there have developed traditions
of fashioning and maintaining decidedly *American* ethnocultural communities and identities, and of pressing for recognition, respect, and just
rewards, along with accompanying responsibilities. In most cases, these
traditions have not been committed to the breakup of the nation but to
the extension of the coverage of its principles, opportunities and rewards
of citizenship and justice to *all* its recognized and respected peoples as
a necessary means to achieving peace and harmony. Extending opportunities to persons of previously excluded and underrepresented ethnocultural groups and working with them to create self-fulfilling prophecies
of success even while requiring that they meet the same rigorous standards as all other participants (contrary to widespread popular beliefs,

there is neither a necessary nor a practical requirement that affirmative actions in behalf of people of color result in any lowering of appropriate standards either for admitting such persons into education programs or for certifying that they have completed them), are crucial manifestations of commitments to cosmopolitan cultural pluralism. The results of these efforts, properly pursued, require and can help to nurture the values and practices appropriate to a civic identity without which our nation will never be likely to make good on its commitment to *e pluribus unum*: to make one nation out of many, that is, to establish a unified, well-ordered, just, and harmonious nation-state out of many nations, races and ethnic groups.

If Nathan Glazer is right, then the off-and-on influence of the tradition of cultural pluralism is now firmly on and widely established. This is a victory worth celebrating, not one to be accepted grudgingly, provided we accept the limitations of an impoverished assimilationist civic identity that required individuals to renounce their ethnocultural identities and, thereby, to forego the conservation and reproduction of their ethnocultural communal groups. In doing so we might be guided by the insightful wisdom of W.E.B. Du Bois who, in speaking to the Association of Social Science Teachers in 1960,[2] argued forcefully, but with careful nuance not often seen in discussions of matters of race in America, that Negroes, for many years into the future, must maintain racial organizations. However, he took care to note that doing so "will be voluntary and not compulsory. It will not be discriminatory. It will be carried on according to definite object and ideal, and will be open to all who share this ideal. And of course that ideal must always be in accord with the greater ideals of mankind" (Du Bois 1973, 152). Du Bois went on to urge the teachers to consider another, especially insightful commitment which, in my judgment, is utterly crucial for all to consider, particularly those of us (Supreme Court Justices included) who worry or are convinced that "discrimination" on the basis of race or ethnicity is wrong *tout court*: "But what American Negroes must remember is that *voluntary organization for great ends is far different from compulsory segregation for evil purposes*" (Du Bois 1973, 152, emphasis added).

For most of his long and productive life as a publicly engaged researcher and scholar dedicated to social transformation to achieve justice and peace, Du Bois was a convinced racial cultural pluralist. Yet, as indicated in the quotes from a speech he delivered and published just three years before his death, he took particular care to urge his listeners and readers to join commitments to racial organizing and institution-building to commitments to ideals of universal brotherhood and sisterhood, to universal human rights. In being committed to cultural pluralism or to multiculturalism, we must also accept responsibility for always attending to the

---

[2]The speech, "Whither Now and Why," as noted by Herbert Aptheker, was delivered to the 25th Annual Conference of the Association during April 1960, and subsequently published in the *Quarterly Review of Higher Education Among Negroes*, July 1960, 28:135–141 (Du Bois 1973, 165).

very real, if not always likely, dangers of divisiveness and, in the extreme, of national dissolution, that result from inappropriate indulgence of ethnocultural groups and their identities. Due regard must be given to our being both beneficiaries as well as stewards of the ongoing experiment in forming a unified nation-state out of many of the world's peoples, thus to the necessity of our all sharing and helping to cultivate and live a shared identity as Americans. In short, as "multiculturalists" we must be cosmopolitan cultural pluralists who are also enlightened liberal republicans. Then, as nursing caregivers, researchers and scholars, we must serve our nation-state as we serve our own ethnocultural communities; and serve our communities and our nation-state as we serve those who are not members of our particular ethnocultural communities. Preparing such persons is a significant challenge for those responsible for programs of nursing education as well as for those committed to supporting their efforts. It can be, as well, an exciting challenge, one that is at the very heart of the American experiment. Let us be persuaded to rededicate ourselves to taking it on.

References

Du Bois, W.E.B. 1973. *The education of black people: Ten critiques 1906–1960.* Edited by Herbert Aptheker. Amherst, MA: The University of Massachusetts Press.

Glazer, Nathan. 1997. *We are all multiculturalists now.* Cambridge, Massachusetts: Harvard University Press.

Smith, Rogers M. 1988. "The 'American Creed' and American identity: The limits of liberal citizenship in the United States." *Western Political Quarterly* 41: 225–251.

Smith, Rogers M. 1993. "Beyond Tocqueville, Myrdal, and Hartz: The multiple traditions in America." *American Political Science Review* 87(3): 549–566.

Tocqueville, Alexis de. 1835 [1990]. *Democracy in America, Volumes I & II.* New York: Vintage Books.

Part Three

Ethical
and
Philosophical
Issues
in
Nursing

8

Ethical and Psychosocial Issues for Minority Nurses

Michael Pallak,
PhD

Faye Gary,
EdD, RN, FAAN

Bobbie Perdue,
PhD, RN

This chapter explores psychosocial issues critical to successful transitions into professional nursing and graduate programs. These issues are especially salient and relevant when considering the recruitment, retention and graduation of ethnic nurses. Since institutions make choices about these issues and about steps necessary to implement nursing programs, we conclude with a discussion of ethical perspectives and principles that are implicit to decisions about program priorities.

As noted elsewhere in this volume, ethnicity is woefully underrepresented in healthcare in general, and in nursing specifically, relative to the general population. Ironically, this means that predominantly White majority institutions and faculty must face the challenge of developing successful strategies for enhancing ethnic participation in health, nursing and education. Yet institutions and faculty suffer from inertia (innovation and change is a slow social psychological process) and often operate from implicit and often unexamined assumptions that may combine to reduce the probability of successful ethnic transitions into the profession. The issue is more than unexamined assumptions and an absence of commitment to systematic integration, since there may be an unawareness of issues that can emerge.

One anecdote helps to illustrate the issue of implicit assumptions, unexamined differences in viewpoint, and unawareness of emerging issues. At one school of nursing, a decision was made in response to external pressures to increase the number of ethnic faculty (and students) over several years. Unfortunately, little prior reflection took place in that the existing White, senior faculty had offices on one floor with little space left for new faculty. As a result, newer and predominantly ethnic faculty received offices together on another floor. The administration's view was that the school could not expect the more senior faculty to disrupt their professional lives by shifting offices. Uniformly, this situation (and this implicit assumption) conveyed an implicit message that ethnic faculty (and students) were not valued and that there was little commitment to enhancing diversity, participation and interaction with new ethnic faculty.

As a result, issues about feeling safe in interactions with the majority faculty and students formed a constant undercurrent among ethnic faculty and students. To be sure, there were other issues within the school regarding ethnic minority participation. But this one example illustrated the problems that ensued when an institution and faculty were unable to acknowledge their implicit assumptions and to empathize with views external to themselves.

This chapter also attempts to demonstrate positive steps by exploring psychosocial issues faced by ethnic students during their transition into nursing programs and into the nursing profession. These issues revolve around the student's internal self-concept in relation to the external environment of academic program, faculty, students and social support. In this presentation we avoid the trap of assuming that every ethnic student is "disadvantaged" (although some may be), that every majority White student is "advantaged" (although some may be), that every White majority faculty member is racist (although some may be), or that every institution is insensitive (although some may be). We underscore that part of the transition task for ethnic students (as is the case for non-ethnic students) is developing a feeling for often quite different cultures, a task that is ongoing for institutions, faculty, and students. At the same time, students continue the personal work and maturation that is part of the transition task for each student. The interplay and resolution of this work contribute to the success or failure in terms of enhancing ethnicity in health, nursing and education.

Given this background on the topic, we move to more detailed consideration of these psychosocial issues in recruitment, retention and graduation of professional nurses.

Recruitment

Schools that are successful in recruiting underrepresented ethnic students employ a variety of multicultural consumer strategies to position their program for ethnic communities. The meta-message is that the school welcomes ethnic student nurses and emphasizes that differences associated with ethnicity, life experience, health beliefs, socioeconomic background, and world views are highly valued. In turn, ethnic students who respond expect financial aid packages, orientation programs, curriculum, academic support programs, and student life programs that embrace core values of equality, diversity, caring, universality, innovation, and quality. For this reason, recruiters have a moral obligation to give students a candid picture of life as an ethnic student. To the extent that these expectations are not met by the student's subsequent experience, disillusion and mistrust will result (Anderson, 1978) and thereby establish corroding influences on both student and program. Hence, the first requirement for an effective recruitment program is honesty.

An effective strategy for increasing the pool of qualified ethnic students is an institutional alliance with feeder schools and community colleges where minority students attend. Through cooperative efforts and peer counselors, respect replaces hostility and the school is more likely to reach ethnic recruitment goals. Schools who consider these strategies could find themselves proposing changes that would actually alter the corporate culture. Planning such changes would need to be integrated into the overall strategy. While seeking advice from community groups may serve a recruitment program well, the faculty who employ such strategies must be prepared to attend to advice that may go counter to their current practices or create discomfort in individual faculty or students still struggling with the changes associated with cultural competence and its expectations. If schools wish to create a safe environment for minority students, they will, of course, first need to conduct an honest assessment of those environmental facts that constitute a danger or source of harm. This assessment alone may reveal substantive issues that will require resolution prior to the recruitment of minority students.

Orientation programs that introduce potential students and their families to the institution lay the groundwork for reality testing about the rules and mores of the institution. When orientations provide opportunities to share the challenges, fears, and excitement of transition, the anxiety about an uncertain future may be reduced. Schools that profess to integrate minorities into the mainstream of campus life should approximate the psychosocial climate of campus during the orientation effort. It is not enough to have a single ethnic administrator or ethnic faculty member available. Rather it is important to have a full array of ethnic professionals participating in the orientation in order for students and their families to feel more at ease.

Orientation programs that are conveniently scheduled on weekends serve as an inducement to many ethnic families. Students enjoy orientation programs that provide them with the opportunity to a) review their financial aid package; b) tour the campus; c) register for first semester classes; and d) understand the psychosocial environment and coping strategies in what is probably an ethnically unbalanced environment.

Based on a survey conducted by one inner city urban university during orientation, ethnic students cite three factors under their personal control that they see as affecting their likelihood of success. These are: 1) having a sense of direction—knowing why they are in college and what career they would choose; 2) having the ability and willingness to organize time and use it effectively; and 3) having or developing good study skills. Three additional factors are interpersonal and also involve elements of the institution: 4) financial resources; 5) personal contact with faculty and staff; and 6) contact with peers. The major factors cited as detracting from the college experience were: 1) family obligations; 2) attending a predominately White school; 3) spending time on special interest activities out of class. Orientation programs that have the major goal of establishing interpersonal trust often use peer advisors in small group sessions where student concerns can be discussed more comfortably. Institutions can then elect to introduce strategies to address the issues identified above as they emerge.

Retention

Other than self-confidence and academic preparation, the strongest determinants of ethnic persistence are faculty involvement, relevant curriculum, social support and financial support. However, few schools actively train faculty as culturally competent teachers, few evaluate culturally competent teaching and classroom learning, and few link cultural competency to tenure evaluations. Nevertheless, the quality of faculty-student interaction plays a major role in both the academic success and the social satisfaction experienced by students and by ethnic students in particular (Donovan 1984). Culturally competent faculty accept multiple world views, incorporate examples from many cultures when teaching health promotion and health restoration and develop meaningful relationships with all students. Culturally competent faculty cognitively challenge students by fostering a spirit of challenging conventional definitions and conventional definitions of health in all aspects.

Competent faculty behaviors listed by ethnic students as affecting learning include caring, respect, honesty and role modeling (Schaffer and Juarz 1993; Windsor 1988; Fitzsimons and Kelley 1996). When culturally competent faculty demonstrate that ethnic students are valued, ethnic students describe a sense of empowerment in the classroom characterized by feelings of belonging. Feelings of belonging are positively correlated with ethnic student retention.

Successful and unsuccessful ethnic nursing students often recall toxic faculty-student interactions characterized by a lack of respect for differences, by the belief that ethnic status is equated with poor academic preparation, by an inability to listen to other perspectives, and by an inability to expand the lens by which to view ethnic health behaviors. Students report that they are often forced to tolerate offensive comments from peers, agency health workers and clients. These students also report that faculty may tolerate or encourage racially segregated and monocultural groupings. Ironically, there is a strong consensus that heterogeneous groupings are more beneficial for teaching tolerance, for solving complex health problems, for exposing inconsistencies in the student's own thinking, for increasing self-confidence and for helping peers build social support networks focused on academic goals (Fullilove 1986). Culturally competent faculty avoid coalition formation with strong students over weak students or with ethnic majorities over ethnic minorities.

Relevant Curriculum

There are three features of nursing curricula that foster responsiveness to ethnic students. The first, that of viewing nursing as a multicultural experience, has been discussed above regarding culturally competent faculty. The second, that of preparing critical thinkers, occurs when programs adopt an integrated model in which domain specific skills are taught along with the courses that students are taking (Langer and Neal 1987). Levin and Levin (1991) note that the integrated skills approach is superior to the developmental approach because it deals with false perceptions that students have regarding the source of their academic problems. While most students consider their problems to be course specific, more often than not the student may have deficits in learning and thinking skills that are basic for content mastery. These deficits may be remediated effectively through planned primary or supplemental instruction in the discipline. Blane (1983) reported that at-risk ethnic students who received supplemental instruction as part of their course offering obtained course grades that were almost one grade point higher than similar students who did not receive such instruction. These students also had a higher retention rate in the following semester as well.

Frierson (1986) conducted a study in which at-risk nursing students were placed in one of two conditions: a) test taking skills only; or b) test taking skills plus cooperative learning groups for added instruction and support. Students in the test taking plus learning group condition outperformed the test taking only condition. Both of these studies lend support to the notion that ethnic nursing students benefit not only from preparatory skills training, but also from the information processing and integrated skills approach (Levin and Levin 1991). Unsuccessful students may compound their problems by "trial and error" approaches such as individual tutoring rather than by approaches based on faculty-student discussion of problem-solving and learning strategies.

The third feature of a relevant nursing curriculum is a proactive intervention program for at-risk students that is fully supported by the institution (Anderson 1978). The proactive intervention usually begins the summer before the student's first year and continues throughout the student's academic career. At-risk students have difficulty recognizing their academic problems. Their self-esteem may be tied to academic progress thereby reducing the likelihood of seeking help. As a result, proactive programs often are mandatory in order to overcome the student's internal denial and conflict. Among the several components of these programs are diagnostic testing to assess academic skills and the necessity for remedial or developmental courses, enrollment in regular college courses in the summer, an early warning system for under-performance, supplemental instruction, peer and professional counseling, career counseling, small group tutorials, test and note taking workshops, and opportunities to develop mentoring and social networks. Participants often have an opportunity to interview ethnic nurses to learn about strategies for success in nursing. The minority student who is not educationally at risk may experience academic success, yet find that faculty make assumptions about the student's potential or competence that are linked to stereotypes or assumptions. Such concerns add another dimension to retention challenges for minority students.

Relevant curricula link faculty and students early in the college experience. Gateway courses are one strategy as is the proactive intervention program with discipline-specific content in a critical-thinking and integrated skill model. The latter provides opportunity for faculty involvement with ethnic students to develop specific coping strategies. While many of these strategies apply to all students at risk, it is wise for any given faculty to carefully assess the degree to which the unique challenges facing the minority student are exacerbated by the added pressure of being a student who is academically at risk. The impact may be more geometric than arithmetic in proportion. Curricula that directly and honestly address the deterrents to cultural competence that schools may actively embrace as a goal, yet never be able to implement, may help the minority student to understand some of the challenges that he or she faces, whether as an at-risk student or not. Curricula that fail to incorporate the substantive historical evidence of systematic racism in the United States, which, of course, includes racism in health care practices, leaves the minority student suspicious of the institution, which may then represent to the student the dominant culture that has historically engaged in these practices and perpetuated them.

Social Support

Social support is defined as the degree to which the individual's needs for socialization, tangible assistance, cognitive guidance, social reinforcement and emotional support are met through interaction with the social network (Hirsh 1980). Marshall (1989) suggested that social support constitutes the most important source of success for ethnic students and attributes the lack of social support to such feelings as alienation, isolation, anger, hostility and rejection among ethnic students. Fitzsimons and Kelley (1993) point out that family support, mentors, teamwork, peer support and supportive relationships with faculty are critical to student progress and retention. Quarry (1990) found that the family was identified as the most important support system for African American nursing majors. In general, the family coached the students and encouraged them to think in terms of future goals, to picture an end in view and to work toward completing tasks.

The dilemma represented here is that ethnic students may regard family obligations as a distracting burden, while, based on Quarry (1990), relying on families for social support. As a result, counselors who work with ethnic students should understand this potential dilemma and facilitate strategies that enhance the family alliance and that balance the burden of family and academic demands. Strategies may involve recruiting additional resources, e.g., to help with shopping, child care, etc., or helping families understand the student's need to devote hard work to the nursing program. Nursing majors need a great deal of understanding and encouragement in order to manage the pressure that they are under.

During college, students develop new support systems with peers for emotional, moral and academic support that effect retention of ethnic students. As a result, student advisors, tutors or peer counselors have been used in: 1) new student orientation; 2) dormitory life; 3) personal-social problems; 4) study skills; and 5) subject matter tutoring (Allen 1988). Subject matter counseling in small groups has appeal because students are more likely to a) become aware of flaws or inconsistencies in their own thinking; b) increase their self-confidence and self-esteem in the process of observing, listening and helping peers; c) build a social support network centered on academic goals (Levin and Levin 1991), and d) are less likely to be socially isolated.

Brown (1977) documented that trained student counselors were given higher ratings by students than professionals. Students counseled by other students showed significant positive changes in study orientation, subject knowledge, grades, and had fewer residual study problems than students counseled by professionals. Perkins and Kemmerling (1963) reported an increase in self actualizing behavior for students participating in groups led by students. In school based programs, students with peer tutors or counselors were rated as either improved or very improved at a higher rate than those counseled by faculty. A higher percentage of students preferred to discuss personal problems with peers. At risk, first-year students who received peer counseling, etc., had a dropout rate that was only one-third that of comparable students without peer counseling, etc.

Mentor support also has a positive influence on ethnic retention. Ethnic mentors in nursing can be recruited from various ethnic nurses associations, churches, sororities, alumnae, as well as from professional and civic associations. Well-developed mentor programs should help majority institutions replace alienation with attachment since mentors assist the institution in helping students manage their life on campus. The strategies mentioned here are important for a successful program; therefore, schools would be wise to take them seriously.

Graduation

The large gap between White and ethnic student graduation rates, and between ethnic enrollment numbers and ethnic graduation numbers, suggests that most schools may not have implemented adequate steps for ethnic students. While this puzzle may not be resolved soon, implementing steps based on psychosocial issues should elevate graduation rates. In many ways, ethnic student graduation is closely tied to institutional commitment, faculty support, academic resources, counseling activities, and to the student's willingness to take responsibility for their own education.

Depending upon student attributes and institutional attributes, some students will take longer than others to meet graduation requirements. Flexible curricula that accommodates faster and slower paced scheduling is desirable. In preparation for graduation, ethnic nurses should be connected with ethnic professionals who can continue to support their growth, development, and orientation to the profession. Ethnic students will still need support as they prepare for the NCLEX, and should be encouraged to set aside specific times for individual review and group study.

There are a number of responsibilities that will accompany the ethnic graduate who is expected to play an active, if novice role in the community and the profession. The graduate should plan to use career placement services, social networks, faculty and clinical contracts in order to secure a position and to join a professional nursing organization, including one of the respective ethnic nurses associations. New earning power may place the graduate in a different social class. This may increase the quality of life for oneself and family, rather than provide a basis for materialistic vanity. As a citizen of the world, we encourage the graduate to support ethnic neighborhood organizations and health care initiatives. We strongly encourage the graduate to return to school within a few years to obtain an advanced degree in nursing and to prepare for a leadership role in the delivery of heath care to persons of ethnic status.

Ethical Perspective in Nursing and Healthcare

Institutions make choices about program, recruitment, and retention strategies in health and in nursing. These choices are grounded in various assumptions both implicit and explicit. We discuss several ethical perspectives in order to provide a context for institutional choices and institutional policy. At the outset, among other things, academic institutions are agencies of socialization that perpetuate a world view about people, health care, education and ethical priorities in the process of molding nurses for the future. Ethical perspectives are explored in this context because the decision of administrators and/or faculty to actively move toward more proportional enrollment, when the lack of proportionality in the past has been demonstrated, is an important one. The question must, of course, be squarely confronted: Is the historical lack of parity based on inequity or injustice, and if so, how do we create alternative conditions and why we do so? What is our moral choice in this situation?

Ethical principles and theories are methods that we use to aid in decision-making in health care. An ethical theory is an attempt to develop a coherent system of principles which are used to guide what people ought and ought not to do. An ethical framework should permit evaluations of actions and moral judgments (Beauchamp and Childress 1994). In health care, codes provide general guidelines regarding moral norms, e.g., "do no harm," or guides for confidentiality between patient and professional. Similarly, discussions about veracity, promise-keeping and autonomy are being advanced (Beauchamp and Childress 1994; Veatch 1989).

Ethical principals including autonomy, beneficence and justice have emerged as guides for decision making in health care. We describe these and focus on justice in a discussion of equal opportunity and fairness regarding recruitment and retention of ethnic nurses. We propose a discussion of equal opportunity and fairness as a component of justice, and link justice to recruitment and retention issues. We assume that there is an agreement that there should be proportional representation of ethnicity in health care and an enhancement of diversity. This shifts the focus to mechanisms for achieving proportional representation such as those discussed above for orientation, recruitment, admission and retention. Such program changes can be implemented without threatening current or past students or program integrity, and these changes enhance current programs by enhancing proportional representation. In short, quality programs insist that ethnic nurses participate in all aspects of health care delivery and health care education.

Autonomy

The principle of autonomy emphasizes respect for persons in that individuals have intrinsic value with a capacity to make rational choices independent of any special circumstances that may determine value. For autonomy, the individual needs both a capacity for self-governance and for control over internal and external processes and affairs. In respecting individual autonomy, health care professionals must believe that ethnic people are entitled to decide their own destiny and to accept the consequences of their decisions. Autonomy is basic for human dignity (Kant, in Beauchamp and Childress 1994; Varga 1984). All ethnic groups should be able to exercise autonomy and thereby experience dignity (Beauchamp and Childress 1994).

Problems arise when the use and boundaries of the principle of autonomy conflict with other moral principles such as beneficence and justice. For example, should ethnic nurses be recruited and retained in nursing programs until their numbers reflect those in the general population? Would such steps reflect the ethic of autonomy in nursing?

Beneficence

The principle of beneficence implies that a person should do good by actively promoting good, kindness, and charity by abstaining from injuring others, by assisting other's progress and by preventing harm. The principle also implies that it is morally wrong not to increase another's good when one is able to do so. Preventative health care and public health interventions are based on this conviction. For example, governments assist each other with the eradication of communicable diseases such as smallpox, measles and so forth. Beneficence requires a sense of generosity in moral terms and is considered a virtue but not a duty by some. Therefore, the act of sharing access to health resources is based on individual and social ideals relating to duty and obligation (Beauchamp and Childress 1994; Menzel 1990; Veatch 1989). Beneficence provides a context for nurse leadership to recruit and retain ethnic nurses. While beneficence is an important principle for undertaking steps for improving opportunity for ethnic nurses, the principle of justice should be part of the ethical equation.

Justice

The principle of justice is attractive because it implies that people should receive what they deserve and includes a sense of fairness and equitable treatment. What happens when people are denied justice over time? How do we determine the appropriate course of action?

Distributive justice represents the equitable distribution of goods, services, rights and responsibilities within a society; e.g., voting, free speech, etc. (Beauchamp and Childress 1994). Thus, burdens and benefits are distributed, e.g., paying taxes, serving in the armed forces, the right to a social security check, and the right to a quality education.

Further, justice implies that similar cases be treated similarly. A common thread in all theories of justice is that programs and services designed to assist people of a certain class must be available to all members of that class. The central issue is whether justice is served when some people are provided access to specific programs while other, equally qualified people, are denied access to those programs.

Principles of distributive justice may be summarized in several ways: (1) to each person an equal share; (2) to each person according to individual need; (3) to each person according to their rights; (4) to each person according to their societal contributions; (5) to each person according to their individual effort; (6) to each person according to their individual merit (Beauchamp and Childress 1994; Deloughery 1994).

Theories of Justice

There are several theories of justice that help to provide perspective for definitions of distributive justice. Among these are Egalitarian, Libertarian and Utilitarian theories. The Egalitarian approach suggests that individuals should have equal access to goods, services, burdens and benefits.

Rawls' (1989) concept of justice emphasizes fairness with society having an obligation to extend programs correcting for various disadvantages. Within health care this might be represented by programs to treat or prevent disease and disability, and that promote good health. In a similar fashion an adequate education is fundamental for well being in society.

Libertarian theories emphasize rights to social justice and stress freedom in economic activity. In other words, people have the right to own, buy and sell the products of their efforts as they wish. Thus people select to contribute to society however they choose and the benefits/ burdens are received in proportion to effort and contribution. Thus, individuals would be free to buy private health insurance and society is not viewed as morally responsible for health care for individuals and families (Beauchamp 1994; Childress 1989; Deloughery 1995).

In contrast, Utilitarian theories emphasize actions that bring out the most good to the most people possible. Individuals have rights to social and economic liberty and obligations are enforced by law. In health care, this view would emphasize health programs as facilitating utility, i.e., the most good to the most people possible (Beauchamp 1994; Childress 1989).

These theories of justice provide differing perspectives by which to examine access and participation in health care and education as a right or as a benefit. If education in health care is a right, then ethnic nurses would be entitled to access programs preparing them to meet the nation's health care needs. However, if access to health care education is viewed as a benefit, then access to programs would be viewed as a privilege and as an act of charity granted in some cases to some individuals. As we have seen historically, the latter view offers limited opportunity and has limited impact on health care education and service.

The Distribution of Health Resources: The Equal Opportunity Account

Daniels (in Beauchamp 1994; Childress 1989) suggests that provision of health care should be just and, hence, based on the principle of "equal opportunity." If a view of justice also includes a principle for fair equality of opportunity, then educational institutions have a responsibility for facilitating the education of ethnic nurses as part of their routine program.

Based on the view of justice as equal opportunity, Daniels (Beauchamp 1994; Childers 1989) argues that simple elimination of formal or legal barriers is not sufficient when seeking employment, education or health care. Social barriers of race, ethnicity, class, gender, social status, etc., continue to influence access to opportunity. Diminished access to health care leads to diminished access to education and, hence, to perpetuation of ethnic disparities in health, well being and advancement. As a result, society needs additional steps to facilitate and enhance opportunities for those disadvantaged by social barriers that determine inclusion in, or exclusion from, health care, education or employment.

In this view, if an individual's current health or educational status is even only in part the result of social barriers to opportunity (within society's political, cultural and social system), then it follows that increased opportunity is needed for fairness and justice. In short, barriers not under the individual's control should not be the sole determinant of opportunity, reward or success (Beauchamp 1994; Childers 1989).

In addition, it becomes imperative to counter the effects of the de facto "natural lottery" on health status that results from poor health resources or inadequate educational opportunities. Since many diseases have socioeconomic, class, or ethnic clusters, these steps and actions are consistent with the principles of justice and utility. As members of the nursing profession, we need to articulate these principles as part of a stringent and cogent plan for increased opportunity in, and access to, health care and education for ethnic groups in our nation.

Principles of justice, when planning programs in the context of psychosocial issues, provide a framework by which to explore issues of opportunity and outcome for ethnic and non-ethnic students, nurses, programs and society. The nursing profession also operates within boundaries of many other systems that shape opportunity and outcome.

Schools who seriously wish to implement changes in their recruitment and retention of minority students will discover that there are moral principles of import that guide the change in their programs and many viable tools to help make the change happen. What is perhaps most challenging, of course, is the personal will of deans, faculty, and indeed the entire institution to make these changes happen. Institutions must be ready to weather the potential storms created by introducing change that, over time, may ask more than might initially have been apparent. If we want to change, we can and we will.

References

Allen, W. 1988. Using paraprofessionals as a retention resource. In *Black Student Retention*, edited by M. Long and C. Ford. Springfield: Thomas.

Anderson, E. 1978. A retention design applied to an Equal Opportunity program. *New Directions for Student Series* 1: 37–46.

Astin, A. 1985. *Achieving excellence in education*. San Francisco: Jossey Boss.

Beauchamp, T. 1994. Principles of biomedical ethics. 4th ed. New York: Oxford University Press.

Bennett, C., and J. Hen. 1984. A conceptual model of Black student attrition at a predominately White university. *Journal of Education Equity and Leadership* 4: 173–188.

Blane, R., DeBuhr, and D. Martin. 1983. Breaking the attrition cycle: The effects of supplemental instruction on undergraduate performance and attrition. *Journal of Higher Education* 54: 80–89.

Brown, W. 1977. *Student-to-student counseling: An approach to motivating academic achievement.* Austin: The University of Texas Press.

Buchanan, A. 1989. Justice: A philosophical review. In *Cross cultural perspectives in medical ethics: Readings*, edited by R. Veatch. Boston: James and Bartlett Publishers.

Childress, J. 1989. *Autonomy in cross cultural perspectives in medical ethics: Readings*, edited by R. Veatch. Boston: Jones and Bartlett Publishers.

Courage, M. M., and K.L. Godbey. 1992. Student retention: Policies and services to enhance persistence to graduation. *Nurse Educator* 17(2): 29–32.

Crawford, L. A., and B.H. Olinger. 1988. Recruitment and retention of nursing students from diverse cultural backgrounds. *Journal of Nursing Educator* 27(8): 379–381.

Deloughery, G. 1995. *Issues and trends in nursing.* St. Louis: Mosby.

Donavan, R. 1984. Path analysis of a theoretical model of persistence in higher education among low income Black youth. *Research in Higher Education* 21: 258.

Fawcett, J., and R. McCorkle. 1995. *Successful postdoctoral research training for African American nurses.* Washington, DC: American Academy of Nursing.

Fitzsimons, V., and M. Kelley. 1996. *The culture of learning.* New York: NLN Press.

Fleming, J. 1981. Special needs of blacks and minorities. In *The modern American college: Responding to the new realities of diverse students and a changing society*, edited by A.W. Clickering. San Francisco: Jossey-Bass.

Frierson, H. 1986. Two intervention methods: Efforts on groups of predominately Black nursing students' board scores. *Journal of Research and Development in Education* 19: 18–23.

Frierson, H. 1989. The impact of testing skills intervention upon Black nursing students' licensure examination performance. *Journal of Negro Education* 51: 82–91.

Fullilove, R. 1986. Seeing the leaks in the pipeline: Improving the performance and persistence of minority students in college. Unpublished manuscript. Berkeley: University of California.

Heydman, A. 1991. Retention/attrition of nursing students: Emphasis on disadvantaged and minority students: In *Review of research in nursing education*, edited by P.A. Baj and G. M. Clayton. New York: National League for Nursing.

Hirsh, B. 1980. Natural support systems and coping with major life changes. *American Journal of Community Psychology* 8: 159–172.

Huch, M. H., R.L. Leonard, and K.U. Gutsch. 1992. Nursing education: Developing specification equations for selection and retention. *Journal of Professional Nursing* 8(3): 170–175.

Jones, S. H. 1992. Improving retention and graduation rates for Black students in nursing education: A developmental model. *Nursing Outlook* 40(2): 78–85.

Jonsen, A. 1980. Do no harm. In *Cross Cultural Perspectives in Medical Ethics: Readings*, edited by R. Veatch. Boston: Jones and Bartlett Publishers.

Ladson-Billings, G. 1992. Culturally relevant teaching: The key to making multicultural education work. In *Research and multicultural education: From the margins in the mainstream*, edited by C.A. Grant. Washington, DC: Faloner Press.

Lang, M., and C. Ford. 1988. *Black student retention.* Springfield, IL: Thomas.

Langer, M., and J. Neal. 1987. Strategies for learning: An adjunct study skills model. *Journal of Reading* 31: 134–139.

Leininger, M. 1995. Culture care theory, research and practice. *Nursing Science Quarterly* 9(2): 71–78.

Levin, Mary, and Joel Levin. 1991. A critical examination of academic retention programs for at-risk majority college students. *Journal of College Student Development* 32: 323–324.

Lillie-Blanton, M., and A. Correa-Alfaro. 1995. *Summary Report: In the nation's interest: equity in access to health care.* Washington, DC: Joint Center for Political and Economic Studies.

Marshall, J. 1989. Students attrition is lack of support or key? *Nursing* 37: 176–178.

Mandel, H. P., and S.T. Marcus. 1988. *The psychology of under-achievement.* New York: Wiley & Sons.

Meleis, A. I., Hall, J.M., and P.E. Stevens. 1994. Scholarly caring in doctoral nursing cation: Promoting diversity and collaborative mentorship *Image* 26(3): 177–180.

Menzel, P. 1990. *Strong medicine: The rationing of health care.* New York: Oxford University Press.

Myers, C., and S. Drevlow. 1982. A dropout intervention program for minority and low income students at the University of California, San Diego. Paper presented at the annual meeting of the American Educational Research Association, New York.

Noddings, N. 1988. An ethic of caring and its implications for instructional arrangements. *American Journal Education* 96: 215–230.

O'Neil, J. A. 1995. Ethical decision making and the role of nursing. In Issues and Trends in Nursing, edited by G. Deloughery. St. Louis: Mosby.

Ormeaux, S. D., and E.A. Reddings. 1990. Gain: A successful recruitment and retention program for disadvantaged students. *Journal of Nursing Education* 29(9): 412–414.

Patterson, A., and W. Seddlocck. 1984. Differences among minority student background and attitudes toward a university and its services. *Integrated Education* 22: 95–110.

Perkins, R. J., and R. Kemmerling. 1983. Effect of paraprofessionals led assertiveness: Training on levels of assertiveness and self-actualization. *Journal of College Student Personnel* 24: 61–66.

Quarry, N. E. 1990. Perceptions of Black adults about their academic progress in a baccalaureate nursing program. *Journal of National Black Nurses' Association* 1(2): 28–36.

Ramsey, C. E., and J.C. Thompson. 1994. Mentoring: A professional commitment. *Journal of National Black Nurses' Association* 7(1): 68–76.

Rawls, J. 1989. The priority problem. In *Cross cultural perspectives in medical ethics: Readings*, edited by R. Veatch. Boston: Jones and Bartlett Publishers.

Rodgers, S. G. 1990. Retention of minority nursing students on predominantly white campuses. *Nursing Educator* 15(5): 36–39.

Saucier, H. L. 1994. Retention of nursing students: Intervention strategies. In *Review of research in nursing education*, edited by L.R. Allen. New York: National League for Nursing.

Schaffer, M., and M. Juarz, M. 1993. An ethical analysis of student faculty. *Interaction Nurse Educator* 18(3): 25–28.

Scott, S. 1992. Educational specialist: Grant-funded instructional and clinical support for minority and high-risk nursing students. *Journal of Nursing Education* 31(1): 40–41.

Shaw, Kenneth. 1991. Diversity on campus: Welcoming new minorities. *Educational Record*. (Winter): 8–13.

Sutton, L., and K. Clayton. 1992. Enhancing minority nursing student success through a comprehensive retention program. *Association of Black Nursing Faculty Journal* 3(2): 31–37.

Tanner, C.A. 1990. Caring as a value in nursing education. *Nursing Outlook* 38: 70–72.

Thurber, F. H., A. Hollingsworth, L. Brown, and S. Whitaker. 1989. The faculty advisor role: An imperative for student retention. *Nurse Education* 14(3): 27–29.

Tucker-Allen, S. 1991 Minority student nurses' perceptions of their educational program. *Journal of the Association of Black Nursing Faculty* 2(3): 59–65.

U.S. Bureau of the Census. 1993. *Current population reports.* Washington, DC: Government Printing Office.

U.S. Department of Health and Human Services. 1995. *Healthy people 2000, midcourse review and 1995 revisions.* Washington, DC: U.S. Government Printing Office.

U.S. Department of Health and Human Services. 1995. *Registered nurse chart book, Division of Nursing.* Washington, DC: U.S. Government Printing Office.

Watson, J. 1990. Caring knowledge and informed moral passion. *Nursing Science*, 13(1): 15–24.

Varga, A.C. 1984. *The main issues in bioethics*. Rev. Ed New York: Paulist Press.

White, W., and W. Biglan. 1982. Information systems approach to admissions, instruction, and retention of college students with a developmental log. *Journal of Research and Development in Education* 15: 16–26.

Windsor, A. 1988. Nursing students' perception of clinical experience. *Journal of Nursing Education* 26(4): 150–154.

Younger, J., and M. Grapp. 1992. An epidemiologic study of NCLEX. *Nurse Elector* 17(2): 24–28.

9

Increasing the Number of Minorities in the Nursing Profession*

Peter I. Buerhaus, PhD, RN, FAAN

I. Underlying Assumptions

It is necessary to first identify my underlying assumptions about how the health care system is likely to evolve over the remainder of this decade and into the early years of the 21st century. I assume the following:

1) Both total national health care expenditures and real annual per capita spending on health care will continue increasing, but the rate of annual increase will steadily decline, nearing a "sustainable" annual rate of between 4 percent and 6 percent per year.

2) Individuals will pay more out-of-pocket for health care and, therefore, will be much more sensitive to the price of health services than they are today. Purchasors (i.e., employers, government and individuals) will select health providers, plans, and delivery systems not only on the basis of price but on empirically measured quality, clinical outcomes, and how effectively purchasers respond to their needs.

3) The majority (80 percent or more) of the U.S. population will be enrolled in some form of managed care, and most managed care organizations will be affiliated with an integrated health care delivery system.

4) Integrated health care delivery systems will slowly but steadily develop such that, from the *patient/consumer's* perspective, there is true administrative and clinical integration (which is not the case today). Fee-for-service medical care will steadily decline. Most integrated systems (not just medical plans) will be capitated and, thus, organizations either

*Taken from a Meeting Held in Conjunction with the National League for Nursing, New York, October 11, 1996. The opinions and conclusions are solely those of the author.

owned by the system or contracting with it will become cost centers. Not only in integrated health delivery systems, but among all providers, financial incentives will become increasingly aligned. Organizations, physicians and nurses will share common financial goals and be held financially accountable for meeting them. Providers will directly bear financial costs if they fail to keep enrollees and entire populations well.

5) The vast majority of integrated health care delivery systems will be competing with other integrated systems for capitated contracts. Ten years from now I expect competition will be based on price and routinely measured and publicly available data on quality. Measures of quality will be far more meaningful and more comparable than what exists today. Consequently, health care organizations will bear direct financial risk if they use anything other than the least costly and highest quality health care workers to produce personal health care services.

6) Prevention and wellness-oriented health care will be more highly valued and become a visible focus of health care delivery. Individuals will bear increased financial risk for their health-related behaviors in terms of being able to affect the amount of their premium payments, share in bonuses or rebates from health plans, and participate in options for ownership in health systems and plans, etc.

7) The number of Americans without health care insurance will begin to fall slowly as a result of incremental legislation passed by federal and state governments. I do not expect, however, that society will have decided to fully finance the cost of health insurance for all those without it by the year 2005.

8) Relative to most every other health profession, I expect the economic value of nurses will rise over the next 10 years. This will occur even if nothing remarkable is done to change clinical practice, education or leadership capacities. However, if the profession changes in ways that enable nurses to better respond to the needs of purchasers, health care delivery organizations (employers), and society's preferences and needs, then there is a strong likelihood that their value will rise at a rate unprecedented in the history of the profession. New and expanded roles will be created at a very rapid rate for and by nurses, and they will be unable to take full advantage of all the opportunities available.

9) I expect nurses to face competitive threats from other providers, but none more strongly than from physicians vis a vis nurse practitioners. I anticipate many in the profession will not deal as effectively with this threat as they could, mainly because they will concentrate on seeking regulatory/legislative remedies rather than undertaking educational and market-based activities aimed at directly confronting competition from physicians.

10) There will be strong pressures to adopt an integrated patient focus and thus nurses will need to find new ways to work collaboratively with physicians on multidisciplinary teams. The boundaries of the nursing

profession will be tested and re-tested, as will the boundaries of medicine and other clinical providers. Economic pressures will force the professions together in new and unexpected ways, and this will present difficult managerial, clinical, and intellectual challenges. The challenge will be greatest in environments where there are both pressures to compete and pressures to work closer with physicians and other clinical providers.

11)   Over the next 10 years I expect that too many nurses will spend too much time and energy fighting non-winnable battles (e.g., stifling competition from unlicensed assistive personnel) and engaging in short-sighted struggles (e.g., payment for advanced practice nurses on a fee-for-service basis or at rates equal to physicians, pursuing mandatory staffing levels in hospitals, etc.), when they could be using that same time and energy making needed changes in nursing education, practice, and research that are likely to strengthen nursing's value in the eyes of purchasors of nursing services. Unfortunately, these diversions are likely to result in the profession's failure to take full advantage of the numerous opportunities that will be developing in the years ahead. Nevertheless, I believe that ten years from now the nursing profession will have attained a higher profile and impact on improving the health of society than is currently the case.

12)   Over the next ten years, the federal government's role with respect to health care reform will largely amount to: controlling its expenditures by enrolling Medicare beneficiaries into managed care; supporting state initiatives to have Medicaid recipients enrolled in managed care organizations; and, passing federal legislation that ties together disparate state policies/regulations governing health care (e.g., adopting a federal standard for two day stay for childbirth, uniform standards for quality in MCOs). The federal government's strategy will be a largely "bottom up," incremental approach to health care designed to correct failures of the market approach that is reorganizing the production, delivery, and consumption of personal health care services in the U.S.**

Given these assumptions about the near future of the health care system and implications to nurses, set forth below are responses to six questions posed by Dr. Hattie Bessent.

II. Responses to Six Questions Posed by Dr. Bessent

1) *What is my perspective on preferred future roles as nurses prepare for their place in the health care arena?*

Over the next ten years, nursing's *preferred* role would be to occupy more publicly visible and important positions in management and caregiving,

---

**The assumptions are an expansion of a statement provided to Sigma Theta Tau International, during its invitation conference "Arista II, Health People Leaders in Partnership, April 1–3, 1996," Indianapolis, Indiana.

which are aimed at providing appropriate and truly cost-effective health care services wherever care is delivered. Nurses would occupy business roles and actively work at the executive level developing, implementing, evaluating, and marketing the organizational components of integrated delivery systems (nurse clinics, community clinics, home health care, hospice, long-term care facilities and programs, prevention and education services, etc.). Advanced practice nurses (APNs) would manage these entities and be responsible for measuring clinical outcomes, monitoring cost outcomes, negotiating with providers, leading improvement processes, and analyzing data and communicating results to providers. Well-educated, professional nurses would be the key providers of personal health care services throughout integrated delivery systems.

Nurses would be working with system decision-makers in designing the functions of information systems and networks, collecting, monitoring and interpreting cost and quality-related data to nurses and physicians, helping determine what a capitated price could be for a targeted population, and occupying a clinically and financially important seat at the table when contracts are negotiated, etc. I see new roles for nurses serving as the integrated delivery system's principal communicator to enrollees and to the general public. Clinically, I expect nurses would be involved in designing and practicing in innovative programs of care delivery involving health education, case finding, applying information technology in patients' homes, and providing alternative health practices. The development of integrated systems will generate an ever-expanding number of roles ideally suited for nurses to demonstrate their effectiveness in improving health care and managing the organizational components of integrated systems.

In both inpatient and outpatient hospital settings, nurses would be providing better nursing care to even sicker patients than they are today. Over the next decade, nurses would have strengthened their clinical, managerial, and interpersonal skills to ensure that patients receive appropriate care and are transitioned safely out of hospitals and passed into the hands of nurses who will expertly manage the patient and family's recovery in their home or other facility. Nurses would be recognized as economically vital components of an integrated system's ability to minimize the costs of patient care, particularly in hospitals, the system's highest cost center. Nurses would be recognized as leaders in quality improvement, eliminators of waste and inefficiency, and would be accomplishing this without any degradation in its traditional humanistic caring role.

2) *Given the rapid changes in the health care arena, what is your view of the future supply and demand of professional nurses?*

Over the foreseeable future I expect the demand for nursing personnel will continue to increase for two reasons. First, society's overall demand for health care will continue to rise, as will total expenditures on health care, and both will exert a positive effect on demand for nursing personnel. Secondly, all things considered, I anticipate that when most health care organizations make employment decisions regarding the number and mix of nurses to employ, they will increasingly recognize the higher value of RNs and APNs relative to other nursing personnel and potential nurse substitutes. As organizations pursue their economic interests under increasingly competitive and capitated environments, they will be strongly motivated to employ only those health workers who can attain the greatest output, at the highest quality, and at the least cost. These criteria will drive employment decisions in all sectors of the nurse labor market for years to come. Given their capabilities and flexibility, I expect these economic pressures to favor strong employment growth for RNs and APNs.

With regard to hospitals, the largest sector of the nurse labor market, I expect overall employment growth will decline relative to the rate of employment growth in other sectors of the nurse labor market. The percent of the nation's employed RNs working in hospitals may fall to somewhere around 55 percent. This does not imply, however, that the total number of RNs working in hospitals will necessarily decline from current levels. In other words, I would not be surprised to find that the total number of RNs employed in hospitals will be the same or even higher than the levels currently employed. The reasons I am optimistic about future hospital demand for RNs include: (1) hospitals will need to take care of increasingly ill inpatients and outpatients, (2) purchasors' growing demand for higher quality hospital services and improved clinical outcomes; (3) continued technological innovation which requires highly skilled nursing personnel; (4) consumer expectations that care will be provided by professional nurses; and (5) hospitals integration efforts to develop home care, sub-acute care, nursing homes, etc. all of which will require more RNs. Nevertheless, relative to other sectors of the nurse labor market, which are growing fast and employing more and more RNs, I expect the *percentage* of all employed RNs working in hospitals to fall gradually over the next ten years.

Although home health care providers' demand for nurses will continue increasing through the remainder of this decade, I anticipate that the demand will moderate as federal and state governments attempt to constrain the rapid rate of spending growth on home health care. Similarly, most other sectors of the nurse labor market are likely to experience fairly strong growth, especially managed care organizations and providers of alternative living arrangements for older Americans, such as assistive living facilities. However, I expect the demand for RNs in the nursing home sector to lag behind other non-hospital sectors due largely to the economic structure of the nursing home industry.

In sum, I believe overall demand for RNs will increase and expect fairly strong shifts in employment from hospitals into ambulatory and community-based settings.

Unlike forces driving the demand for RNs, those affecting RN supply present a more complicated and uncertain picture. The supply of RNs consists of two different components, the **short- and long-run supply**. The short-run supply of RNs is concerned with (1) the willingness of existing RNs to participate in the nurse labor market and, (2) the number of hours existing RNs work. The long-run supply of RNs is concerned with the number of RNs that will be available to the nurse labor market at any given point in time in the future. Both the short- and long-run supply of RNs are influenced by different forces which interact and can exert opposing or reinforcing affects. In addition, the forces affecting short- and long-term supply are influenced by changes in the demand for RNs.

With respect to the short-run supply, the current national average RN participation rate (the percent of all RNs who are working in the labor market) is at historically high levels (around 83 percent), and over the past three decades the average number of hours worked has increased. I wonder, however, if there is any room for participation rates to increase further and how much additional labor supply (hours of work) are available from the current supply of RNs? Because the participation rate is so high, I worry that if RN wages do not increase, or if there is a dramatic positive surge in the national economy, that many RNs who have been working at such high levels of output during the 1990s would leave the nurse labor market. In addition, the RN workforce is aging rapidly and research shows that older RNs work less hours relative to RNs younger than 25 years of age. This effect would decrease the short-run supply of RNs. Moreover, the aging of the population could mean that more RNs will be caring for their parents, which will reduce the amount of time available for RNs to spend in the labor market.

To some extent, these negative effects could be offset if more men and minorities were to become RNs, particularly because studies show that minorities work more hours on a weekly and annual basis than their white counterparts. For example, using data from the *1988 National Sample Survey of the Population of the Registered Nurses* (N = 10, 264), married men, Asians, Black, and Hispanic RNs worked 309, 248, and 258, and 92 more hours per year than their white counterparts (Buerhaus 1994). Similar results were found in an earlier study based on data from the 1984 national survey (Buerhaus, 1991). Yet, over the past two decades there has been little progress in increasing the number of RNs who are minorities.

Economic effects and short-run supply

Because over 70 percent of RNs are married, spouse income exerts a strong influence on RNs' decision to participate in the labor market and their decision on the number of hours to work. As the national economy has strengthened over the 1990s, more Americans are obtaining a greater sense of job security and beginning to experience increases in real earnings. Rising incomes among RN spouses, however, could cause RNs to decide that they can afford to work fewer hours or even withdraw from the labor market altogether (Buerhaus 1993, 1995). The opposite situation, the economy sinks unexpectedly, could drive some RNs who are not participating in the labor market into the market. Thus, what happens to the general economy will exert an important affect on the short-run labor supply of RNs in the near term. Unfortunately, no one knows how the economy will fare or how strongly the effect will be on changing RNs' employment activity.

Another uncertainty affecting the short-run supply of RNs concerns changes in RNs' earnings. Real (inflation adjusted) RN wages have been flat since 1991 (Buerhaus and Staiger 1996). Should the economy strengthen and wages in non-health care sectors rise (like some economists expect in the near term), then the upward pressure on wages is likely to spill over into the health care sector. If health care organizations raise RN wages, then this could stimulate some existing RNs to maintain or increase their work activity by shifting from part- to full-time or working over-time. Nonparticipants may even decide to rejoin the labor market. At the same time, however, having to raise wages would increase employers' costs and thereby create an incentive to employ fewer RNs. (In a competitive market employers are motivated to reduce their labor costs.) Unfortunately, it is difficult to predict what will happen to RN wages and the net effect on RN employment.

Long-run supply of RNs

With respect to the long-run supply of RNs (the *future number* of RNs who will be available to the nurse labor market), a similarly vexing array of forces will determine the number of new RNs produced over the next ten years. Among the most important forces include: the wages paid in the nurse labor market (higher wages stimulate increased enrollments into nursing education programs, and vice versa), tuition rates charged by nursing programs, the capacity of programs (spaces available), availability of faculty, changes in graduation rates, social changes influencing the desirability of nursing as a career, and the number of RNs leaving the workforce through death or retirement. How these forces interact determines the future number of RNs available to the nurse labor market.

A new concern affecting the long-run supply of RNs concerns the effect of the aging of the RN workforce. Since 1984, the average age of RNs has been increasing rapidly, and the number of RNs under the age of 30 has fallen precipitously. Results of RN labor supply studies (Buerhaus 1994a) show that older RNs work fewer hours than younger RNs, holding the effects of other variables constant. For example, using RN data (N = 14,506) from the *1988 National Sample Survey of the Population of RNs*, RNs between the ages of 30–44 worked between 140 and 204 fewer hours per year than those under the age of 25 years. RNs in the age groups 45–54 and 55–64 years worked 152 and 305 fewer hours per year, respectively. Very similar results were reported in an earlier study using the *1984 National Sample Survey of the Population of RNs*

(Buerhaus 1991), and in other studies (Bognanno, Hixson and Jeffers 1974; Link and Settle 1981). The conclusion drawn from these short-run labor supply studies is that the number of hours available to the labor market decreases substantially as RNs become older.

Replacing the aging RN work force with new RNs is likely to present a daunting problem in the near future. Demographics trends and other forces are likely to reduce the number of future RNs, a problem already being compounded by recent declines in enrollment in undergraduate nursing programs. Much more research needs to be done to understand the implications of a rapidly aging RN workforce.

Over time, it has generally been the case that nursing education programs have been able to respond to changes in the nurse labor market in a reasonable period of time. Given the rapidly changing market structure of health care, however, it will be essential to ensure that the labor and education markets pay closer attention to the signals emitted from each other. To the extent that both are corresponding and working toward the same goals, the long-run supply side of the labor market will be better able to respond effectively to the changing needs of employers. To ensure this, however, nurse education programs must acquire good faculty and be able to quickly adjust their curriculum so that they can prepare students capable of practicing cost-effective nursing in all health care settings, particularly within the reality of managed care.

Finally, the adequacy of the long-run supply of RNs is clouded by what I perceive to be a miss-match in the output of nursing education programs (too many associate degree graduates compared to baccalaureate graduates) when one considers the current and emerging needs of employers. I do not know what the proper mix of associate to baccalaureate degree nurses should be. I suspect, however, that no harm to society or to the profession would be done if output from associate degree programs were scaled back considerably and baccalaureate output increased proportionately.

In sum, although I expect the demand for RNs and other professional nurses will increase, what happens to the short- and long-run supply side of the nurse labor market is difficult to project. Both components of RN supply require careful monitoring to anticipate and spot trends so that appropriate policy actions can be developed. Research shows that men and minorities work more hours than comparable white RNs, a labor market dynamic that should be considered when formulating policies aimed at increasing the number of minorities in nursing.

3) *How will a market-driven health system impact nursing?*

The short answer: Profoundly!

I have attempted to address this issue elsewhere (Buerhaus 1992, 1994b, 1994c, 1996, 1997), but essentially the effect comes down to the following: A well developed market in health care will reward employers (the demanders of nursing services) who minimize the price of health care, improve the quality and outcomes of care, and satisfy and respond to changing consumers' and purchasers' expectations and preferences for health care. In health care, organizations that come up short in these areas will risk going out of business. Accordingly, because delivery organizations employ professional nurses (RNs) to produce health care services, RNs will have to provide managerial and clinical services that explicitly and visibly contribute to the organization's ability to minimize costs, improve quality and outcomes, and increase its capacity to respond to consumers and purchasers' ever changing needs. If RNs fail in this regard, organizations will find alternative workers to help them accomplish their goal of economic survival. In a more competitive environment RNs will constantly need to make choices on the kind of care they give knowing that they will increasingly bear the direct financial and employment consequences of their decisions.

A market-driven system will cause RNs to confront the above economic realities and at the same time live up to the profession's traditional care giving role and obligations to society. Philosophically, I see no conflict between the two. A market-driven health care system simply provides the incentives that compel nurses to demonstrate how their actions and interventions (which carry economic and non-economic costs) contribute meaningfully to improving quality and outcomes as well as lower costs. These behaviors should be important to members of the profession no matter what incentives or market structure (a highly regulated or competitive market) exists. To the extent RNs fulfill these requirements, a market-driven system will reward them through favorable employment opportunities and earnings.

4) *Is there any way nurses can protect their practice to ensure quality care?*

More than anything, nurses must fully understand that a well developed market-driven health care system (which we do not yet have, and may not attain for some time) will reward providers who minimize costs and improve quality. Further, RNs must realize that even the lowest cost provider is unlikely to survive if purchasors perceive its quality has fallen below some threshold. Moreover, nurses need to bear in mind that Americans have always insisted on high quality of health care and there is no reason to suspect that this will change in the future (consider the numerous organizations and groups dedicated to this goal that have emerged in recent years). Unlike most economic transactions, buying health care services is a very personal experience; people are sensitive to both the quality and price of the service. Given these dynamics, I see RNs, and the profession in general, having a comparative advantage over many other health professions for the following reasons: (1) RNs enjoy a favorable reputation for quality; (2) RNs are not seen as a primary source of the high cost of health care and are therefore not a target of public mistrust; and, (3) the public counts on RNs to uphold, protect, and improve the quality of health care. Nevertheless, the nursing profession can not afford to take these current advantages for granted. Society is permitting the development of market-driven incentives to change the health care system because there is an expectation that it will obtain more value for its tremendous expenditures on health care. Thus, if the profession fails to live up to the demands of a market-driven system, then it will risk losing its favorable public opinion and support. The message to the health care system and to those who earn their livelihood providing health services is clear: change and improve your performance.

There are some specific actions that the profession and individual RNs can do to minimize the threats and increase their chances of doing well in a competitive environment.

First, leaders in nursing, especially those involved in policy making bodies, need to take more responsibility to ensure nurses acquire a broader and deeper understanding of the health care system, how it is changing, why it is changing, and the opportunities and challenges facing nurses. Nurses need to understand the incentives that drive markets, what the positive and negative dimensions of market competition are in general and as applied to health care. Moreover, they need to appreciate the difference between financing problems and economic problems, and which problems can be handled through regulatory, legislative, taxation, or market approaches. To illustrate, many nurses believe economic competition in health care is "bad" because it will not resolve problems surrounding the uninsured. They do not realize that for the most part providing health insurance to those without it is a financing problem remedied by society deciding, via our political system, to subsidize the acquisition of health insurance. It is, therefore, unfair and inappropriate to evaluate a competitive market on the basis of whether it addresses the uninsured population, something it is not designed to do.

This is but one example of how, in my experience, nurses adopt uninformed views about competition. Economic competition is sweeping the land, and if nurses have unfounded predispositions about competition, then they will be less likely to see and act on the opportunities that competition will present. Equally important, they will be intellectually unprepared to take constructive actions that will be needed to address the problems that will arise from a more competitive market.

Nurses should take actions that are aligned with the underlying forces that are transforming health care and not work against them. Nursing should stake out a leadership role by working to reduce waste, eliminate duplication, increase efficiency, and simplify and improve all aspects of clinical care and the systems and organizations that support clinical activities. Such actions are not only beneficial to employers and consumers, but are consistent with nursing's social obligations and are in the self-interest of the profession because they raise their value and hence their economic attractiveness to employers.

Nurses, especially staff nurses, should take the initiative to develop new relationships with administrators on topics centered around quality and lowering costs. Nurses could engage employers by asking them what they need to know about how nurses contribute to quality, and then set about obtaining answers. I do not believe large federally sponsored studies are needed to find the answers; rather, they can be found in the work place by nurses entering into new relationships with other clinicians and administrators and jointly developing projects to find better ways to improve the quality of services and clinical outcomes. The same needs to be done with respect to nurses finding new ways to lower the cost of producing nursing care.

Finally, I believe the nursing profession would do well to accept the inevitability of a sustained period of transformation in the financing and delivery of health care. The highest responsibility of leaders is to help nurses realize the nature of change, manage it, work through the anxiety and pain it will produce, see and take advantage of opportunities, and help nurses acquire the skills and knowledge they will need to participate more effectively in shaping the health care system. Although there will be set-backs and unpleasant periods through the rest of this decade, the economic discipline fueling the transformation of health care delivery will steadily manifest itself in ways that reward organizations and health professionals who create the highest value for purchasers. As excess capacity is eliminated from the health care system and some nurses lose their jobs (temporarily), nurses must stay focused on what purchasors' value from them and keep trying to provide it. Nursing's leaders in education, research, service, and policy need to stay focused on issues related to increasing nurses' value and avoid the temptation of trying to preserve the status quo. As long as nurses are seen as contributing to an organization's ability to lower costs and improve quality and outcomes, nurses' value will rise relative to others and more will be employed than would otherwise be the case.

5) *Given the inability of the profession to delineate levels of practice, what will be the fallout of the baccalaureate prepared nurse?*

I do not expect that leaders in nursing education will be able to solve this problem. Nor do I think they necessarily should, because I expect them to solve issues surrounding delineation in a way more likely to satisfy their constituents. Besides, I see signs that the problem is beginning to be addressed elsewhere—in the nurse labor market.

There are increasing reports from the field that managed care organizations and hospitals in competitive markets are demonstrating their preferences for more highly educated baccalaureate RNs by employing them over associate degree nurses. In other words, certain sectors of the labor market are giving signals that they perceive baccalaureate RNs are more valuable than less educated and more plentiful associate degree RNs. However, some questions come to mind: How strong are these signals and how widespread are they? Why exactly are baccalaureate graduates being preferred over associate degree RNs? Will nursing educators in associate degree programs and their financiers pick up on these signals, and if so, how will they respond?

With regard to any fallout for baccalaureate-educated nurses, they will be positive rather than negative. Labor market demand for baccalaureate degree RNs is likely to increase relative to associate degree nurses, and thus I expect this preference will be communicated to individuals considering a nursing career. In turn, this should result in upward pressure on the demand for baccalaureate graduates and softer demand for associate degree graduates.

6) *What is my perspective on the future of advanced practice and graduate (Masters and Doctoral) prepared nurses.*

If I could invest my money in APNs, then I would move as much as I have into them. From nearly every perspective, their stock is rising!

Some people are worried that in response to the sudden and positive interest in APNs, nursing education programs are producing too many APNs. This position assumes that one knows precisely how many APNs should be prepared, which I do not believe is this case. If given the choice, I would recommend that too many APNs be produced. (In either case, having either too few or too many APNs imparts certain costs and benefits to nursing, employers, and society.) Although an excess supply of APNs would place downward pressure on their earnings potential, this negative outcome could be offset by increased employment, as more APNs would be demanded at lower wages than would otherwise be the case. Further, increased employment would facilitate opportunities for the American public to become more comfortable receiving health care from APNs. This, in turn, is likely to lead to raising expectations that APNs should be full members of the health care team regardless of the health plan or delivery system. If this economic scenario unfolds, than an excess supply of APNs could have considerable positive effects.

The downside I foresee is the possibility that APNs could get caught up in their new found attention and believe that they are safe from the pressures of having to constantly seek out new ways to lower their costs and improve their quality and increase their responsiveness to consumer's and purchasors' needs. Thus, it is worthwhile to consider how pressures could be exerted on schools producing APNs to make investments in improving the quality of their education. APN programs will need to stay up to speed with the rapid changes enveloping their graduates, and to an increasingly competitive and expanding supply of primary care physicians and physician assistants.

Turning to masters and doctoral education, I believe educators need to do a much better job preparing graduates to practice in the 21st century.

In my view, graduate (and undergraduate) educators can make a great contribution in helping raise the value of nurses. Educators need to dedicate themselves to preparing nurses to be the leaders of clinical quality improvement and cost reduction. Unfortunately, there is a substantial shortage of faculty and nursing curriculums that are able to produce the kind of nurses needed by tomorrow's employers. Addressing this shortcoming is urgently needed.

An entirely new curriculum needs to be developed and taught around the economics of capitation, business practices for nurses, clinical practice skills, information systems, quality assessment, outcomes measurement, primary care in a capitated payment arrangement, etc. Courses now being taught such as "nursing care of children" should become "nursing care of children under managed care"; "nursing care of adults under managed care"; "nursing care of communities under managed care", etc. As more Medicare and Medicaid beneficiaries are enrolled in managed care, I expect nurses will play many new and expanded roles. Similarly, as more medical group practices, hospitals, and other components of integrated care systems become capitated, nurses will become vital to the economic survival of these organizations. In addition, nurses will need to improve their existing strengths providing culturally-relevant and competent care. Thus, nurse educators need to understand what future roles are likely to be and prepare nurses to fill them. Occupying meaningful roles is the best way to change and improve the system.

The focus of doctoral education in nursing should place a greater emphasis on directly benefiting the profession. Doctoral education and research in most clinical disciplines are undertaken to address practice related problems. However, in nursing the majority of dissertation research is aimed at testing propositions of nursing theory, hopefully yielding results that can help build the knowledge base of the discipline. Although important, given the nature of the changes in health care and the challenges facing nurses, doctoral programs need to develop the discipline's capacity for conducting research that helps practitioners understand relationships between nursing activities and quality of care and to clinical and system outcomes. Doctoral education could assist professionals with problems concerning the boundaries of the profession brought about by organizations emphasizing patient focused, rather than discipline focused multidisciplinary care delivery teams. Practitioners will need help dealing with the challenge of preserving the nursing perspective and sorting out responsibilities with other disciplines.

References

Bognanno, M., Hixson, J., and J. Jeffers. 1974. The short-run supply of nurses' time. *Journal Human Resources* 12: 86.

Buerhaus P. 1991. Economic determinants of the annual number of hours worked by registered nurses. *Medical Care* 29(12): 1181–1195.

Buerhaus P. 1992. Nursing, competition, and quality. *Nursing Economic$* 10(1): 21–29.

Buerhaus, P. 1993. Effects of RN wages and non-wage income on the performance of the hospital employed RN labor market. *Nursing Economic$* 11(3): 129–135.

Buerhaus P. 1994a. Short-run labor supply of registered nurses. Unpublished paper. 1994. Harvard University.

Buerhaus, P. 1994b. Economics of managed competition and consequences to nurses: Part I. *Nursing Economic$* 12(1): 10–17.

Buerhaus, P. 1994c. Economics of managed competition and consequences to nurses: Part II. *Nursing Economic$* 12(2): 75–80, 106.

Buerhaus, P. 1995. Pressures building in the hospital employed RN labor market. *Nursing Economic$* 13(3): 137–141.

Buerhaus, P. 1996. The value of nursing care: Creating a new place in a competitive market. *Nursing Policy Forum* 2(2): 13–21.

Buerhaus, P. 1997. What is the harm in imposing mandatory hospital nurse staffing regulations? *Nursing Economic$* 15: 66–72.

Buerhaus, P, and D.Staiger. 1996. Managed care and the nurse labor market. *The Journal of the American Medical Association* 276(18): 1487–1493.

Link, C., and R. Settle. 1981. Wage incentives and married professional nurses: A case of backward-bending supply? *Economic Inquiry* 19: 144–156.

10 The Impact of Economics on the Minority Nurse

Myrtle K. Aydelotte, PhD, FAAN

How will the minority nurse fare in the future world of economic uncertainty? What will be the impact of changes in the economy upon her reimbursement, professional security, and what will be the demands placed upon her to increase productivity? How is this to be achieved concomitant with the expectation that she will maintain performance at a high level while holding cost low? These are only a few of the questions confronting the minority nurse of today and tomorrow. To answer them requires general knowledge of the economics of health care.

Any consideration of health care economics involves three sets of demands: the demands of society for health care; the demands of organizations that are established to address those demands; and the nature and expectations of the nurse supply which is involved in response to the first two demands. The interaction of these three are highly complex, complicated, and ever changing. These three sets are interactive in that changes in an element of one brings about changes in each of the other, forcing an accommodation of some sort, which has economic ramifications. (Figure 1) An understanding of the forces which operate in the economics of the health field is basic to the nurse's maneuvering in the world of work.

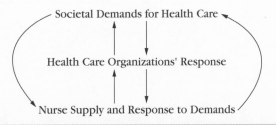

Figure 1. Interactive Model of Health Care Demands

The Impact of Economics
on the Minority Nurse

The movement toward global production of materials and the development of markets for them have had a major impact upon healthcare worldwide. The work force is no longer restricted to that of the United States and purchasers of both healthcare and products are world wide. Health problems of each nation, use of child labor, unsafe working conditions, human rights, sanitation, and the like have been brought sharply into the awareness of U.S. society. One obvious force operating in the demand for health care has been the rapid spread of the HIV/AIDS epidemic. Other epidemics and natural disasters have also initiated international attention for health care services.

In the United States, the forces giving rise to demands for health care services are many. A major one is the change in population demographics, such as increases in the aging and aged populations; the shift in number of births and the rate of infant mortality within specific population groups; death rates in specific populations, such as those resulting from murder and suicide; and growth in the numbers of ethnic/racial groups. Marked shifts in the numbers of population arranged by age groups have two possible effects. One is an increase in demand for healthcare for a specific population, such as the sudden increase in births. The other is related to the availability of human resources which may be sharply reduced through the deaths of a group essential to providing manpower, such as that which occurs in wars and in epidemics targeting specific age groups.

In the United States the current and projected increase in the aged population is placing heavy demands for maintenance care of the elderly and hospice care for those in the terminal stages of life. The aging and aged are the most rapidly expanding portion of the American population. Of these, persons over 85 years of age is the fastest growing segment and will double in numbers in the next twenty years (Reif and Martin 1996, 3). By the year 2000, there will be about 35 million Americans aged 65 or older and will reach 40 million by the year 2010. By 2030, there will be more older adults than children (Gallagher 1995, 8). From 1993 to 2018, elderly users of nursing facilities is projected to increase from 2.2 million to 3.6 million and users of homecare will grow from 5.2 million to 7.4 million (Gallagher 1995, 7). Nearly 10 million people are disabled and with the increasing aging populations this number will correspondingly grow. Currently, three of five persons (60 percent) with disabilities are elderly (Gallagher 1995, 10).

Changes in minority populations, especially in the Afro-American and Hispanic populations, are increasing demands for care. The U.S. Bureau of the Census projects that by the end of the first quarter of the 21st Century, 38 percent of the general population will come from racial/ethnic minorities. By the middle of the 21st Century almost half of the population will be from these groups (NACNEP 1996, 5).

Often unrecognized as a major force in the demand for health care are those characteristics which relate to people's standard of living, their cultural beliefs, their expectation of treatment and services, their view of care as a "right" or as a privilege". Changes in per capital income and societal wealth impact demand. As individuals carry health insurance, the demand for health care services increases. Introduction of new technology, new drugs, or different medical interventions and treatments, as these become known through the media, result in new demands.

These forces converge to create a situation that poses questions of economic importance. How much of its resources, both human and nonhuman, is society willing to invest in the delivery of health services? How will the resources be allocated? What is the payoff and the risk for the respondents?

Health Care Organization Response and Arrangement for Services

The response to society's demand for health care appears in a set of institutions to provide it and mechanisms to finance it. Predicted for the year 2005 is a modest growth in health services employment resulting in total job growth. Employment of registered nurses is expected to grow faster than the average of all occupations through the year 2005 (p. 6).

The prediction of modest job growth is the result of organizational maneuvers to met the demand while maintaining control of costs. Various forms of organizations and practices are emerging to provide primary care, prevent illness, and foster change of life style. These, along with new medical technology and computerization, are leading the shift from traditional hospital based services to other settings, including the formation of major medical networks and systems made up of clinics, practitioners' offices, surgical centers, free standing laboratories, long term facilities, and home care services. Many are resulting in national chains for profit. These systems and networks are being quickly put into place. The practice of providing intensive care and treatment of highly critically ill patients in hospitals is continuing but the length of stay for each episode is short. The services for recovery and rehabilitation is given in out-patient settings. Thus, hospitals are becoming high intensive centers with a comprehensive set of other types of units offering various services attached to them. As a result, the number of hospital beds has decreased 15 percent over the last decade and outpatient visits has increased by 64 percent (NACNEP 1996, 12).

Demands are also leading to major changes in the institutions and organizations providing for long term and home care. Traditional nursing homes are introducing new nursing units, such as those caring for patients with Alzheimers, Aids, and those who are dying, hospice units. Many have added Adult Daycare units. With the length of hospital stay for patients shortened and surgical and diagnostic procedures being performed in outpatient settings, other nursing homes are turning to transitional services. These provide nursing care on a short term basis until the individual can care for himself or herself. Home care services have also grown rapidly. Various types of agencies have developed under differing leadership and management. Concern is being expressed about the quality of care they offer and the prediction is that in the near future increased attention will be given to improvement of this sector of care.

Response to the demand for health care involves both human and nonhuman capital and requires money for both. Money is required for the construction and maintenance of the physical plant, equipment, technology, supplies, and employees. Money for these are secured through federal and state government programs and grants and through private sources and insurance plans. The drive to reduce health care costs, maintain quality of results, and to respond to purchasers for improvement of care has resulted in government initiatives and enrollment in managed care plans. The growth of managed care either by private insurers or by the enrollment in some states of Medicare and Medicaid participants has led to economic competition among managed care organizations. The evolving economic forces resulted in downsizing of hospitals, but there is no evidence that managed care has led to a slowdown within sector wage growth. In a study of seventeen states with high HMO enrollments, the investigators found that nurses had no problem in securing employment, turning to jobs in nursing homes, clinics, offices, and home health care. In the seventeen high enrollment states, the employment and earnings grew more slowly than elsewhere (Buerhaus and Staigner 1996).

Employers consider several factors in determining the employment of nurses. The major objective of employers is to combine as economically and as effective as possible the necessary capital and personnel to produce the needed services and treatment. To do this, they explore the price of personnel, that is, the total compensation package, including benefits. To determine how many nurses are needed, then, requires an analysis of the total compensation package for nurses and the comparison of it with that offered to other types of employees. The analysis includes making a judgment of what nurses can provide in relation to what other types of workers can provide; the nurses' contribution to the quality of services; and the desired clinical outcomes for the patients and clients. Also added to the equation is the available supply of nurses—the total number, types, education, experience, and the amount of competition offered by nearby institutions. While making decisions about how many and what kind of nurses to employ, the employer faces other questions. These are related to the expectations of the clientele, the mission of the institution, regulations imposed by government, the nature of the technology required, and the risk involved in over staffing, under staffing, and the use of combinations of personnel.

The balance between total compensation costs for nurses and revenue earned by the institution is a major consideration. As earnings increase, there is a tendency to at least maintain or increase the numbers of nurses dependent upon indicators of quality and satisfaction of the care provided by nurses. As total compensation of nurses increases, there is a tendency to decrease numbers of registered nurses or offer other combinations of nursing staff.

The objective function of the policy and decision makers of health care institutions is to maintain a balance between cost and achievement of mission or between cost and preservation of the image the decision makers wish to project. On one hand, there is the need to provide quality of services, and on the other, to minimize cost, increase efficiency, and meet competition from others. Since physicians are often perceived by organizational leadership as the agents who attracts sources of revenue, that is the patients and purchasers, the relationship of the institution to physicians also enters in making decisions relating to cost, employment of personnel, and expenditures of money for equipment, supplies, the physical plant, and the like.

The forces impacting an organization are very complicated, originating in both the external and internal world of the institution. The value of nurses and nursing to the institution as seen by the decision makers is critical to the economic well being of the nurse.

The Nurse Supply and Response to Demand for Services

The number of registered nurses, their availability, and the types of practice they offer enter into the decision of an organization to purchase their services and in what amount. Availability is dependent upon several factors, such as geographic location, family responsibilities, marital status, total family income, age, financial obligations, standard of living, and competing occupations of other types of work which the individual is capable of doing. The influence of these factors may vary from time to time and are, in fact, not under the control or influence of the organization seeking to employ the nurse.

The supply of registered nurses is dependent upon the number of students who are admitted to schools of nursing, complete the program, and qualify for a license to practice. The recruitment of students, then, is critical to maintaining a continuous supply of registered nurses. The size of the registered nurse supply is also dependent upon the retention of nurses in the work force. Nurses leave the work force for several reasons—family responsibilities, age, change in financial status, disillusionment, death, and personal reasons.

The number of registered nurses employed as reported in March 1996 was an estimated 2.2 million. Of these, the majority are employed in hospitals. Over the past decade, the number of registered nurses working in hospitals increased 11.6 percent, but of this number, only 5.5 percent of the increase were working in in-patient units. The great growth, 68 percent of the increase, was in out-patient service (NACNEP 1996, 12). Greater growth, 74 percent, has occurred between 1988 and 1992 in home care (NACNEP 1996, 14).

The education of 25 percent of the 2,239,816 registered nurses were initially at the baccalaureate level, but of the recent graduates entering the field, 31 percent had that type of preparation. Fifty-nine were associate degree graduates and 10 percent held the diploma (NACNEP 1996, 15–16). Of the number who went on to earn a higher degree, 52 percent were generic baccalaureate graduates (NACNEP 1996, 19).

Only 9 percent or an estimated 206,835 of the 2.2 million registered nurses in March 1992 were minority nurses (NACNEP 1996, 20). Compared with the total minority population, this number of minority nurses is far from proportional to the total population of their minority group and is inadequate in number to care for those requiring care (Table 1).

With the exception of the Asian/Pacific Islander nurses, the education of minority registered nurses were not very different from the proportion of white, non-Hispanic nurses. The Asian/Pacific Island nurses were most likely to be baccalaureate graduates. Of the black nurses in 1992, about 10 percent had masters of doctoral degrees as compared to white, non-Hispanic nurses and 6 percent in other racial minority groups (NACNEP 1996, 20).

A major concern about the registered nurse supply is the aging of the workforce. In 1988, the average age of the employed registered nurse was 39.4 years. In 1992, the average age was 41 years. The number of registered nurses in the age group under 30 years of age decreased by 20 percent between 1988 and 1992 (NACNEP 1996, 17). Worthy of note is the fact that newly graduated baccalaureate nurses tend to be younger than those who completed associate and diploma educational programs.

One of the major attractions to any professional or occupational field being considered by potential entrants is the remuneration to be expected as one of its practitioners. In 1994, the median weekly wage of full-

Table 1. Population of Minorities and Numbers of Minority Nurses

Groups	Black	Pacific Islander	Hispanic	American Indian/ Alaskan Native
Total[a]	33,389,000	9,653,000	28,438,000	NA
Nurses[b]	90,611	73,785	39,441	8,986

[a]Source. Current Population Reports, Series P60. Income Statistic Branch, HHES Division, U.S. Bureau of the Census. U.S. Department of Commerce. Data as of 1995.
[b]Source. National Advisory Council on Nurse Education and Practice. Report to the Secretary of the Department of Health and Human Services on the Basic Nurse Work Force. U.S. Department of Health and Human Services. Health Resources and Service Administration. Bureau of Health Professions. Division of Nursing. 1996. p. 20.

time salaried registered nurses was $682. The middle 50 percent earned between $542 and $838 weekly. The lowest 10 percent earned less than $395 weekly; the top 10 percent, $1008. The University of Texas Medical Branch survey of hospitals and medical centers reports the median salary for staff nurses, based on a 40 hour week and excluding differentials, to be $35,256 in October 1994. The median salaries for other registered nurse professionals ranged from $50,700 to $73,444 (p. 16) (Table 2).

The supply of the registered nurse workforce has historically undergone cyclical variation in numbers. When the number of registered nurses in the workforce falls, salaries rise. Likewise, when the number rises, the reverse occurs and the salaries fall.

In the changing health care environment, now being experienced, a major concern is the nurse's ability to provide the type of care needed to serve the clientele. There is a need for nurses who are prepared with essential knowledge and skill to render community based care. Also needed are those who can provide technologically complex intensive acute care for patients undergoing episodes of critical illnesses. The rapid growth of minority populations necessitates the need for a richer diversity of ethnic/racial mix of registered nurses to meet their health care needs with the cultural and ethnic expectations of those populations.

Predictions are that prospects in nursing are good and that many new positions will result. Growth of nursing positions is expected in all sectors and, if the trend toward utilization and reimbursement of advanced nurse practitioners by institutions and managed care organizations continues (Canavan 1997, 1), the growth in this specialty will be pronounced.

Although the supply of nurses may be good and future prospective work pronounced as growing, several issues are apparent that have

Table 2. Median Annual Salaries of Registered Nurses In 1994[a]

Position	Annual Median Salary	Range of Salaries
Staff Nurse (hospitals)	$35,256	$28,531-$43,711
Staff Nurse (nursing homes)[b]	$32,200	$29,200-$35,400 (middle range)
Head Nurse	$50,700	
Clinical Nurse Specialist	$47,674	
Professional Nurse Practitioner	$47,432	
Nurse Anesthetist	$73,444	

[a]Source. Occupational Outlook Handbook Home Page. Bureau of Labor Statistics Home Page. Howard N. Fullerton, Jr. Bureau of Labor Statistics. February 25, 1996. p.5.
[b]According to Buck Survey conducted by the American Care Association, reported in the above source.

economical ramifications. Fewer registered nurses available tend to raise salaries unless substitution of other types of workers can produce results of equal value. This implies that the work performed by any other type of worker must not have the same clinical value as that carried out by the nurse, if the registered nurses wishes to maintain her position in the organization. In other words, the professional nurse must maintain exclusive knowledge and skill required to produce the results and the work must have significant value to the organization to warrant her employment. If she does not demonstrate her superiority in producing results of value, the employer, because of economics, will select a worker who requires less pay.

The other factor having economic impact on the nurse is her capability to adapt to changes in the organization's focus of services it selects to provide. The recent down-sizing of hospitals, that is the shift from acute in-patient services and shorter hospitalization to out-patient services, nursing homes, and home care services has been economically driven. For the same reason, some clinical services have been eliminated and others combined and computerization has been introduced. These changes have resulted in dislocation of nurses, some of whom were unprepared to adapt or to learn new skills. Many nurses fail to understand the need for economic survival of the organization and the forces driving the change. The nurse of the future must be adaptable and capable of learning new knowledge and skills, dictated by the economy and patient demands. The concept requires a change in emphasis upon job security, as it is traditionally understood, to professional security. If the nurse is well prepared and flexible, she can find success in the opportunities found in a variety of settings.

The forces operating in the economy and in society call for a major change in the nursing role. The National Advisory Council on Nurse Education and Practice states this well: "The nursing role of the future calls for registered nurses to manage care along a continuum, to work as peers in interdisciplinary teams, and to integrate clinical knowledge with community resources. All aspects of the role are directed toward cost-effective, good quality care. In order to better serve the population of the future, more cultural sensitivity is required as the diversity of the population increases" (NACNEP 1996, 14).

Conclusion

There are numerous forces operating at all levels which have economic impact on the provision of healthcare. Awareness of the complexity of these will help the nurse as she moves along in her career. Unfortunately, data about minority nurses in the workforce are very limited. Not available is information about the types of positions held by minority nurses, their geographic distribution, salaries they earn, experience, and career development. Little is known about the obstacles they encounter as they move along their career paths and the type of discrimination they may be experiencing. Data are much needed to assist in recruitment, retention, graduation, and career advisement.

The impact of economics on the minority nurse can be summarized by making three points. First, the need for well educated nurses is great and employment opportunities will be many. The economic forces in society are creating changes in the healthcare system and as a result systems are enlarging and new ones are emerging. New initiatives will fashion even more new models and nurses will be in demand. Second, as a result of restructuring of the systems and consumer and purchaser demands, changes in nursing roles are taking place. These changes give the nurse the opportunity to demonstrate the economic value of her work. Third, the growth of minority populations is rapid. There is a great need to increase the number of nurses from these populations. Although nursing educational programs emphasize cultural sensitivity, the enrollment of individuals already socialized in the cultural beliefs and customs of a minority group will enrich the total offering and upon graduation, provide much needed services. Well prepared minority nurses can offer the greatly needed leadership in the nursing field and in health. There will be many opportunities for this leadership and by its exercise, minority nurses can make a vital impact on the economics of healthcare.

References

Buerhaus, P.I., and D.O. Staigner. 1996. Managed Care and the Nurse Work Force. *The Journal of the American Medical Association* 270 (November 13): 1487–1493.

Canavan, Katheleen. 1997. Columbia Presbyterian recognizes APRNs as primary care providers. The American Nurse, 29 (2): 1.

Gallagher, Rita Munley. 1995. *Community based long term care-Agendas for the 21st Century.* Washington, DC: American Nurses Publishing.

National Advisory Council on Nurse Education and Practice (NACNEP). 1996. Report to the Secretary of the Department of Health and Human Services on the Basic Registered Nurse Work Force. U.S. Department of Health and Human Services. Health Resources and Services Administration. Bureau of Health Professions. Division of Nursing.

Occupational Outlook Handbook. *Registered Nurses.* Occupational Outlook Handbook Home Page. BLS Home Page. Howard N. Fullerton, Jr. Bureau of Labor Statistics. February 15,1996.

Reif, Laura, and Karen S. Martin. 1996. *Nurses and consumers; Partners in assuring quality care in the home.* Washington, DC: American Nurses Publishing.

*Sources of many of the ideas in this chapter have been drawn from materials prepared by Peter I. Buerhaus, PhD, RN, FAAN, director, Harvard Nursing Research Institute and assistant professor, Harvard School of Public Health, for a presentation at a meeting on Issues related to Minorities in Nursing, National League for Nursing, October 11, 1996. Also useful was a paper prepared by Robert V. Piemonte, EdD, RN, FAAN, Executive Director (retired), National Nursing Students Association, January 1997.

11

Beyond Appearances: The Philosophical and Sociological Issues Confronting Nurse Educators In Response to Changes in Health Care Delivery and Population Demographics

Phyllis Beck Kritek, PhD, RN, FAAN

Few activities drain off the energies of nursing faculty as effectively as that of tinkering with the curriculum. This truism serves for many as a source of bemusement or irritation, but the pattern persists. It is a task we tend to return to like swallows to Capistrano, annually and with predictability. It is important to tease apart this pattern a bit, to understand why it irritates and yet seduces, since the topic of this paper implies the call to yet more change.

Tracing the history of curriculum revision in nursing schools in the United States returns us to Nightingale, perhaps most accessible in her *Notes on Nursing* (Nightingale 1969). Reflecting on the early national curricula might best be understood revisiting Lavinia Lloyd Dock's *Textbook on Materia Medica for Nurses* (Dock 1890), a curriculum heavily focused on disease states as described by the discipline of medicine. Over the ensuing decades one can discover a complex series of changes, most focused on the steady effort to carve out the boundaries of a distinct discipline called nursing. Such a review can reveal much about the evolving content of nursing education. It can also reveal the persisting values.

Whether honored in the breach or not, each curriculum revision sustains a fundamental commitment to the patient, a conviction that the needs of the patient drive the decision processes and the practices of the nurse. Context and content change; the values do not. This fact is noteworthy since each context and content change has required some type of adaptation aimed at sustaining those fundamental values. This paper discusses a context and content change that calls forth the need to once more alter our curricula in ways that manage to sustain our fundamental values about patients, their health, and the nurse's response to these within a given context. These four central constructs of health, patient, nurse and context, consistent components in all nursing theory, have most recently been described as nursing's metaparadigm. With each change, they persist.

Contextual impact can be observed in a progression, in examples such as the impact on immigrant settlement houses, world wars, the discovery of specific drugs and treatments, technologies of trauma, extension of life expectancy, intractable diseases, and possibilities for rehabilitation and recovery. Nursing has often found itself in a reactive posture in such changes; society or medicine change, and nursing responds with an analogous change.

Other changes have been more internally driven, and often reflect the push within nursing to increase its collective sense of self worth and value, in examples such as the introduction of and emphasis on topics such as nursing research, nursing theory, nursing administration and advanced practice nursing. In these latter changes, nursing has selected a pathway, and set out to meet the demands of that choice through change. In such changes, nurse educators change the curriculum in the hope of changing the discipline in some fundamental sense.

There are a variety of ways of creating change in a discipline; we nurses appear to put a marked emphasis on changing nursing curricula as an important resource to that end. We have been less likely, for instance, to create change through mandates issued in the practice setting, firing or disciplining those who fail to comply with a proposed change unless such non compliance threatens patient safety. Thus while some changes in nursing education have been implemented in curricula several decades ago, the practice changes may actually never occur or do so very slowly. The integration of nursing research into practice, or the shift from a medical model of care to a nursing model of care are useful examples. Curricula revision as a primary model of change is an imperfect model at best. Yet we continue to embrace it.

Watching these changes up close and personal, one sees a complex political process where those faculty who embrace or even champion a change lead an initiative toward change: we will now all have an integrated curriculum, we will now all have a curriculum based on this nurse theorist's convictions. Syllabi are revised and/or purged, objectives are rewritten, content is modified, and test questions are recrafted. This process is usually reflected in an impressive array of paper products. We call this the revised curriculum.

Implementation is a messier process. Passive aggressive sabotage of a new curriculum is the most reliable and successful way to keep an unwanted change from happening. I can write all the right words, say all the right things, and ask all the right questions, but if I do not actually endorse the change, it will not happen . . . not in my course. If you stay in nursing education long enough, you can see a variety of models for giving the appearance of changing curricula while never actually doing the deed. It is not hard to do, has no reprisal or consequence, and can even be defended with intellectually sloppy phrases like "academic freedom" or "individual interpretation of the curriculum." Many changes never go beyond appearances; many changes do not happen.

Enlarging the Challenge for Change

I have described this process of curriculum change in nursing because it is the context within which today's changes will occur; it is the backdrop for the observations I will make in this paper. It acknowledges that a highly successful model already exists for resisting necessary change in nursing curricula, one that merely gives the appearance of change without ever getting to the substantive change. Acknowledging this at the outset seems intellectually honest at best, foreboding at worst. The changes needed for our times are larger than discussions of research outcomes or AIDS care, though both are good examples of things we have managed to appear to put in our curricula without necessarily doing so. How much greater is the challenge when the changes of the times reach to some of the most persistent and insoluble problems of our culture.

Drawing a more complete, and perhaps more disturbing picture of the challenge and its context requires that we acknowledge a variety of facts that are rarely openly discussed. When discussed, they are often veiled or excused, and leave the topic once more one of appearances only. The most compelling of these for me is the simple fact that the dominant cultures in the United States, the European American ones, have shaped, defined, controlled and determined the nature and character of health care in the United States, and of nursing. From our British roots to the present day, the patient is invited into a complex system shaped by the European American mind and that mind's definition of reality.

We rarely describe this fact honestly and openly, perhaps because most European Americans tend to not describe this fact as a cultural phenomenon, often not recognizing that their culture's views and values control the dialog and decisions, and that their culture is only one of a given array of possibilities. Without an honest confrontation with or experience of alternate cultures, any given culture believes their own to be the true, right, and real. Difference teaches us the relativity of culture. If indeed one culture dominates a given environment, one can readily believe that this is not merely a culture, but the sole possible definition of reality. It seems embarrassingly naive and narrow sighted, but it is nonetheless true.

Tracing this a step further, if a dominant culture views other cultures as threats, or needs the dominant culture to "win" or "prevail," or if indeed alternate cultures are viewed in some light of inferiority or subservience, then the dominant culture not only may perceive their reality to be the only and best reality, but may also perceive others to be dangerous and irrational threats. I believe this is the challenge of the times and the single most important change that health care and nursing confront in these rapidly shifting times.

Facing Demographic Facts

The United States Census Bureau predicts that while the United States was, in 1995, 74 percent European American, by 2050 that percentage will be 53 percent. Hispanics, who are now only 10 percent of the population, will then be 24 percent. African Americans will grow from 12 percent to 14 percent and Asians from 3 percent to 8 percent. Only Native Americans, now at 1 percent, are predicted to neither increase nor decrease. Newsweek recently reported this as "the nation will be a lot less white and a lot more everything else" (Morganthau 1997, 59). Further reflecting the bias that undergirds these discussions, this is described as being "more ethnic" (p. 58).

Word choice reveals the cultural bias I have just described. Clearly, European Americans, who are designated "whites," do not realize that they are linked to their particular culture and thus ethnicity, despite the fact that such designations exist and are the appropriate ones. European Americans are also ethnics, and their cultures are multiple and varied. They are also described as "White," indicating that the designation focuses on skin color or pigmentation levels. Being "White" is a category, and those outside this category are "everything else," carefully linked to some given culture and designated as not "white." This is a mind set revealing itself, a point of view taken without reflection or self critique because it seems to those who write such comments that none is necessary. White, or European American *is* reality; everything else is something different, not of the reality, an alternative outside the norm. Popular media provide a useful window on the habits of mind and language we embrace.

When you're 95 percent of a population, or 82 percent or even 74 percent, this mind set appears to work, at least while you're in the majority. When those percentages start to shift, things change, as a drive through Los Angeles can demonstrate, where by 2002, European Americans will be the minority, and by 2040, Hispanics will be 50 percent of the population. Marriage across ethnic lines will further confound those comfortable in a European American worldview, and it will become increasingly difficult to "categorize" everyone and keep them in tidy boxes of differentiation, to say nothing of inferiorities and superiorities. Things are changing and they will continue to change.

In a spirit of "appearances," this is often dealt with through an inane series of negotiations designed to give the appearance of adaptation to the change, popularized as "politically correct" language patterns and behaviors. It is reminiscent of the curricular changes on paper, and has about the same impact. Giving the appearance of adaptation is a fairly mindless and limited response to these changes, and one likely to simply prolong the process of substantive change. Being, speaking or behaving in a "politically correct" fashion may reveal more about our fears than give even a modest indicator of the degree to which we have actually coped with the complex issues of race, ethnicity and culture.

Facing Health Care Delivery Facts

The cataclysmic changes in health care in the United States enjoy a wide variety of descriptions, often influenced by the particular world view of the describer. Most, however, would concur that these changes alter the locus of decision-making and give heightened emphasis to the issue of cost. In the former, the physician as the central decision-maker is replaced by the source of funding, the "third party payer." In the latter, the "corporatization" of health care, using an image of "corporate" reflective of the 90s world view in this country, gives lip service to quality but intense attention to cost containment. This combination leads to a decision process where not giving care can be a more compelling motive than giving care.

More ideological discussions of health care change offer additional insights, each enjoying a novel twist when related to cost-containment themes. Some tend to emphasize the shift of power and choice from provider to patient, now called consumer or customer. In this world view, the patient will more and more determine exactly what they want, and "customer satisfaction" will become a central determinate in the nature and quality of services provided. As is obvious, if the services provided are culturally congruent with the patient population culture, this will be a satisfier. Thus, European Americans today may enjoy this satisfier. As demographics shift, cultural congruence will become a cost factor of import.

Another ideological shift, often linked with the World Health Organization's campaign, "Health for All by the Year 2000" increases the emphasis on primary care, illness prevention and health promotion and argues that health programs will thus be community-based and community sensitive. The United States health care system, often touted as the best in the world, has historically been increasingly an illness care system demonstrating extraordinary success in extreme situations such as trauma, transplant and technologies of disease. Hence the shift to community-based primary care is a dramatic and disruptive one, and as the demographics of the communities to be served shift, this complexity will increase. Over the last several decades, community-based care has often been used as a euphemism for proposed health care programs for indigent, minority or underserved communities. It was often assumed that the care would reflect the social status of the population: it would be dealt with as inferior care. When the entire system shifts to community-based care, then the description of community becomes altered.

An emerging effect of cost-containment measures, also ideologically based, is the reality that provider mix will change, and traditional provider hierarchies will deteriorate. On February 7, 1997, the *Wall Street Journal* reported that "one of the nation's leading managed care companies", Oxford Health Plans Inc., had crafted an agreement with Columbia Presbyterian Medical Center in New York wherein nurse practitioners will have primary care provider status, admitting privileges, and will "be paid at doctor rates" (Winslow 1997, A3). The sometimes politically charged relationship between advanced practice nurses and physicians is effectively moved out of the political and into the economic arena where the decision-makers achieve what professional dialog failed to achieve.

A less frequently acknowledged dimension of health care change is one at present controlled almost exclusively by the consumer, one organized medicine finds particularly troublesome. This is the rapid growth and popularity of alternative and/or complementary health care services. These services are often ones more congruent with cultures other than European American, perhaps most easily exemplified by the practices of acupressure and acupuncture which are a dimension of traditional Chinese medicine or the practices of herbology which are a traditional dimension of African and Native American medicine. Historically, these practices were often treated as quackery or occult. Today they are growing enterprises.

Awareness of this shift has been swift and striking, often based on the study conducted by Eisenberg et al. (1993) reported in the *New England Journal of Medicine*. They found that in 1990 over one-third (34 percent) of the citizens of this country sought alternative therapies, and a full 72 percent of this group did not share this information with their allopathic provider. Perhaps more compelling however is the fact that the actual visits to alternative providers (425 million) exceeded those made to allopathic providers (388 million), and were paid for out of pocket at an average cost of $27.60 per visit. These services are sought, and those who seek them return for more. Even the traditional European American boundaries of exactly what health care is are quickly shifting.

The changes in health care chronicled here are not exhaustive, but point to the potential impact such changes portend. What all this evidences is the need for a more ethnically diverse provider population, and the increased competency of all providers in attending to race, culture and ethnicity. Hence, curricula changes become imperative. They do not stem from an impulse toward "political correctness" or even well intentioned "multiculturalism." They are actually economic and political issues that carry a burden of inevitability. Thus, changes are less choice and more imperative, a realization that does not appear to have yet visited the nurse educators "in the trenches." The schools who can move quickly to make these shifts will have the advantage; those who do not will simply drift into a state of anachronism. What was once viewed as European American curricular largesse is quite something else under these contextual givens.

The Philosophical Ground Under Our Feet

Where are the European American nurse educators during all this shifting and changing? The answer is embedded in the philosophical stance taken, whether conscious or not. Walter Truett Anderson, who edited a book called *The Truth about the Truth: De-confusing and Reconstructing the Postmodern World* (1995), describes this state: ". . .we are in the midst of a great, confusing, stressful and enormously promising historical transition, and it has to do with a change not so much in what we believe as in *how* we believe" (p.2). This shift is uniquely European and American in temper, tone, and source, and is often described as the move from modernity to postmodernity, "the situation in which the world finds itself after the breakdown of the "Enlightenment project the project aimed at getting all the world's diverse peoples to see things the same way— the rational way" (pp. 3–4). The project, of course, assumed that there was a single correct mode of representation of reality.

The amplification of the nature of postmodernity has been largely the task of a handful of European and American philosophers. They evoke some fairly intense responses, many angry in tone. Anderson, however, makes a useful distinction concerning the state or condition we find ourselves in—postmodernity—and the "various schools and movements it has produced" (Anderson 1995, 7). You can dismiss or ignore the latter, but the former persists no matter how much you would like it to be otherwise.

We are confronted by a state of "radical relativism," (Anderson 1995, 7) accelerated by sociological forces such as information and communication technologies, global mass economies, ecological initiatives, genetic manipulations, explorations of outer space, and reconstructions about gender. We once believed truth was out there waiting for us to discover; increasingly, we learn that it is a social construction, it is made rather than discovered. This discovery serves as an abrupt wake up call for persons convinced that their particular cultural perspective is the best or only valid one, and the fact that we "made it up" means we can obviously "make it up" in a whole new way.

Anderson posits that there are at least four dimensions to postmodernity: self concept, moral and ethical discourse, art and culture, and globalization. In each, we are moving from the "found" that we perceived to be unalterable truth to the "made" that we humans construct. As we understand this better, the boundaries on our realities shift and we find we can change, eliminate and create anew. We also find that old certainties are now merely today's constructions, and that differing constructions are not by some fiat either better or worse than one's own.

It has been my sense that nurse educators have not yet engaged in the tough intellectual struggle postmodernity demands. It is a rich struggle, with difference and diversity the most compelling factors. It can, however, be framed either as a disturbing disruption and threat or as an exciting opportunity. Ernest Becker has made what seems to me to be one of the most positive statements about the state we're in: "It is one of the most remarkable achievements of thought, of self-scrutiny, that the most anxiety-prone animal of all could come to *see through himself and* discover the fictional nature of his action world. Future historians will probably record it as one of the great, liberating breakthroughs of all time, and it happened in ours" (Becker 1995, 35).

What keeps us from Becker's celebratory view? It has seemed to me that we have not yet unveiled the subtle dimensions of the Enlightenment project that play out in our day-to-day lives in this country. Toulmin (1990) has done a superb job of unearthing some of the dimensions for our perusal in his book *Cosmopolis: The Hidden Dimension of modernity*. Because modernity argued for decontexting, it ignored the humanistic, the oral, the local, the timely, the cultural, the practical, the particular, and the reasonable. This ignorance, however, characterized only those who embraced the Enlightenment project; others found themselves the "target" or focus of the project. Hence, persons who failed to embrace this project were identified as not rational, as in need of "repair." Most analyses of modernity, including Toulmin's, demonstrate this bias where historical context is American and European and entire continents are simply excluded, as if they did not exist during these historical times, or indeed have vital and viable philosophies. Colonization was normative, and is only now winding down to its final death throes. There was only own way to be, think, live, and it was exported through force. This defines some peoples as objects of the project, hence the popular language of the "white man's burden."

The burden, of course, was only so conceived by the white man. Large groups of indigenous peoples did not volunteer to be "saved" and did not perceive themselves to be defective or inferior, in need of salvation. Only one group's social constructions created this perception. Postmodernity has made that clear, and the disorientation for the "white man" is considerable. An example here may be useful. When colonists from the European nations came to what is now the United States, the ethnicity was made up entirely of what is now called Native American or Indian. Now Native Americans are 1 percent of the population. When it was 100 percent, the descriptors of the natives by the colonists included terms such as "savage" and "heathen." While there were exceptions among the colonists in these descriptors, one cannot fail to be struck by the obvious genocide involved in the "white man's burden." It was not just that European Americans wanted to have a universal and single right answer for everything; it was also that one must impose that goal on others, and resistance to such an imposition demonstrated inferiority or defectiveness. It gave persons license to impose a world view on others against their will. The implicit arrogance is striking at best.

Toulmin aptly concludes his analysis with an observation that points to this issue. "Our reflections on the order of society, as well as nature, are still dominated by the Newtonian image of massive power, exerted by sovereign agency through the operation of central force, and we have lost our feeling for all the respects in which social and political achievements depend on *influence*, more than *on force*. For the moment, the varied political relations and interactions between transnational, subnational and multinational entities, and the functions they can effectively serve, still remain to be analyzed, by an "ecology of institutions" that has, as yet, scarcely come into existence" (Toulmin 1990, 208–09). One has to realistically ask if the European American mind is the best equipped to conduct this analysis, given the habits of mind and heart.

Toulmin aptly notes that one may respond to the challenge of postmodernity with either nostalgia or imagination, noting that ". . .the future will reward those who anticipate the institutions and procedures we shall need" (Toulmin 1990, 203). That of course is the point I have been edging toward: that the postmodern mind is better equipped to prepare for the future than the mind that preceded it. And it is my sense that for the most part we have few nurse educators schooled in the difficult challenges of the postmodern mind.

On the contrary, it is my sense that we have, in the main, nursing faculties of European Americans embracing a modernity shaped and framed for them in terms of the "white man's burden," often kindly and well-intentioned faculties, of course, but intellectually constricted into a world view that is germane to an increasingly small percentage of the world population. By way of example, most Asian countries do not concern themselves with either the Enlightenment project or its demise, and are not inclined to struggle with the question of the white man's burden. Yet the premises of modernity shape our teaching philosophies, our education methodologies, our evaluation protocols and our convictions. We are inclined to see through a very small lens, and it is not serving us well today, and perhaps never did.

There are complexities here. Nursing is still largely a woman's discipline. Like many of the "minorities" we serve, we nurse educators are still struggling to break out of the oppressive sexism implicit in the Enlightenment project and the ensuing "white man's burden." We are thus more equipped to understand exclusion, decontexting and the at least the implicit message of inferiority. This is confounded, however, by the fact that we are primarily "white women," the help mates and partners of men who have carried "the white man's burden" with our assistance, support and encouragement. Partnering, for the European American woman, has been more a function of concurring with the Enlightenment project than arguing with it, even when it excluded half of all the partners, women. Hence American feminism, as a movement, often finds itself in a strangely conflicted position where it too wants to further the "universal" answer of the Enlightenment including its distorted images of womanhood, and concurrently claims that difference introduces other realities that demonstrate the inadequacies of the myth of the "one right way." It is not surprising that this is often viewed as feminism for "white women only." And its implicit ambivalence is predictable.

Into this ideological morass, we nurse educators lay claim to the task of enhancing multiculturalism in our curricula, a task that obviously will have an amazing array of meanings, most contingent on the degree to which individuals realize that their world views are simply constructed realities unique to them. We develop programs for "recruitment and retention of minorities" with only a vague sense of some larger picture of the world view of the persons designing the programs or those for whom the programs are intended. We give the appearance of having engaged in a thought process that simply has not yet occurred in many if not most cases. In many cases, we will simply design a "machine" in the traditions of the Enlightenment project, set out to predict and control outcomes, implement our programs, and then become taciturn or angry when the appropriate "minorities" do not respond as planned. That we are using a uniquely European American approach to the issue simply does not occur to us.

How does this look in the concrete? Most often, it seems to me, we sit in the European American perch as if it were the seat of reality and then record observations on how "other cultures" differ, using the European American culture as a norm or standard. Hence, other cultures do or say things differently in the following ways, believe differently in the following ways, etc. In effect, our very effort to begin to deal with multiplicities of culture actually reinforces the assumption that there is a given norm and a collection of deviations. That the norm is just one more permutation simply goes unnoticed.

Framing the Sociological Context

It does not stretch the imagination even a little to see how this philosophical posture embeds itself in the norms and habits of a European American dominant culture, both nationally and within the nation's health care delivery system. Thus, when one culture or another expresses its preferences or desires, they are attended to within that world view, and the most common response is to "adapt," variously stated as "this is how we do it here" or "we have always done it this way." We fail to notice that diversity is really pluralism, and we are all just one version of that pluralistic array. The European American culture is not better or worse; it is just one more version. Indeed, a careful appraisal of European American cultures reveals that there is enormous variance within and among these groups. Diversity can really start looking diverse. Krippner and Winkler (1995) observe that there are many models of human consciousness. Thus, in the construction of worldviews, these all require attention. As Anderson notes, "The universe now seems, if not infinite, at least infinitely complex and mysterious. Our eternal truths now appear to be inseparable from the cultures that created them and the languages in which they are stated" (Anderson 1995, 240). We cannot simply add a bit of content here and a little video tape there and say we have revised our curricula. In a national culture struggling with this change, the social context becomes powerful. If a given enterprise is controlled by nostalgic European Americans who wish we had never noticed any of this, then the changes will not only be appearance only, but will completely miss the larger sociological realities. In a country where racism has proven so resistant to change and such racism is linked to the divide between European Americans and everyone who is not, the social context of such curricular efforts becomes daunting.

This is worrisome for the student of society and social systems. We have crammed our understandings of society into the traditional models of Western science, longing for prediction and control. In contrast, the postmodernist contends that "the most important human activities can barely be measured, much less predicted and controlled" (Krippner and Winkler 1995, 162). Getting everyone open to the idea that things are no longer going to be the same is going to be difficult. Disruptions of world views heretofore perceived as final and absolute will disturb everyone, and as Simon (1995) notes, ". . .there is little likelihood that there will be simple, uniform or comprehensive ways of understanding the potential for distress" (p. 160). This is the sociology of postmodernism we are increasingly experiencing.

Implications for the Curriculum Committee

It seems seductive to advise that the wisest move these days may be simply to resign from the curriculum committee. We all talk a good humanistic message, but having discovered that our constructions of reality are merely that, constructions, we are then called upon to create something new, something beyond the assumptions of a single world view seeking desperately to be the only world view. Some will argue that some things will perdure, though how they know which ones is worthy of its own little deconstruction. Since I anticipate that the resistance to the kind of changes postmodernity presages will be significant (indeed, already is), I am inclined here to give a solemn nod to the nostalgia buffs, and move on to those who are willing to struggle with the call to imagination. What do I do if indeed I want to alter curricula in a way that grapples honestly with the postmodernity that is characteristic of our times? What does such a task ask of me?

Behind Appearances

I think that we will not be able to get beyond appearances until we first struggle with exactly what we have hidden behind the appearances. This can become pretty dicey. We may be far more attached to the familiar, customary and therefore comfortable than we might have imagined. Peeking behind the veil of illusion asks us to take a long hard look at what we are hiding from, and having seen it, to face down our fear, conquer it and stumble toward some broader plane of wisdom. Morihei Ueshiba, the founder of Aikido, states that "The Art of Peace is not easy. It is a fight to the finish, the slaying of evil desires and all falsehood within. On occasion the Voice of Peace resounds like thunder, jolting human beings out of their stupor. (Ueshiba 1992, 35). Curriculum revision may actually have to start with a jolt out of our stupor. Peeking behind the veil may call forth character and courage we had not imagined. We may have hoped to "prevail," to be the "superior" culture, to sustain the status quo. Good intentions will not get us very far; the task is simply too arduous.

And our willingness to take on the challenge may not be welcomed. Because behind the veil we will meet the specter of racism and discover its challenge. Cornel West (1994), in describing the basic aim of his life, states it bluntly: "to speak the truth to power with love so that the quality of everyday life for ordinary people is enhanced and white supremacy is stripped of its authority and legitimacy" (p. xiv, preface). To bring to the curriculum committee a commitment to strip white supremacy of its authority and legitimacy is a daunting task. And as West has so often made clear, while he eloquently speaks his "truth to power with love," it will disturb, disrupt, and sometimes enrage those for whom this authority and legitimacy has primacy. We seem reluctant to simply say this out loud, to look the ugly monster in the face, name it and search our own hearts and souls for the faces of racism and supremacy we embrace. And we will need to change.

Saying these things out loud always seems to me a bit like an invitation to kill the messenger. I wince. I wait nervously for the attack. It seems odd to me. Of course we know that racism in the United States is not yet solved or resolved; of course we know it permeates our culture on every level; and of course we know that it taints our thinking, our acting, our teaching, our conversations with our students, our nursing practice and our institutional practices. Yet we attempt to convince ourselves, each of us in one way or another, that somehow, achingly politically correct, we personally have transcended racism. We alone among all others have risen above the masses, remain untainted, not racist. I have concluded racism is a hydra-like creature, a many headed demon. If I succeed in cutting off one head, another will grow. It is of the fabric of our society. A story may help.

Three nights ago I went to a local restaurant to eat. I was tired, preoccupied, and hungry. I was alone. I wanted to eat, mind my own business, and go home. I wasn't in search of meaningful life experiences or challenges. I was seated in a booth. About three feet from me the restaurant had set up three free standing tables in a row. A large party had been served there, and only four young couples remained, seated on the end nearest my booth. At the head of the table was the celebrant, who was being congratulated for a promotion and concurrently announcing the first pregnancy for he and his wife. Spirits were high, and the group had obviously enjoyed a few pitchers of margaritas.

It was a Mexican restaurant and most of the staff were Mexican American men, many still mastering English as a second language. In exchanges with the staff, the party at this table were polite, even convivial. Out of earshot of the staff, they indulged in a variety of antics, mimics of the waiters accent, bantering ridicule. Eventually they began to discuss a document circulating among them that ridiculed African American speech patterns. They were warming to their sense of the perceived humor in this document. The women at the table did not participate, some looking uncomfortable, one trying to hush the celebrant while his wife looked on a bit nervously.

I sat in my booth trying to figure out what made sense here, how I might best respond to this situation. I felt like a tape recorder in a Texaco executive meeting. I considered leaning over or stepping over and speaking to the group. I knew what I would evoke: appearances, perhaps hostility. I knew I would not evoke a change of heart. As I watched, I became more attentive, and probably signaled the women in the party that I was not bemused. In retrospect, I may have been a factor in their discomfort. I did not imagine, however, that I was altering anyone's values. They lumbered out soon after, essentially unchanged. The hydra had another head.

This tough process of getting to the heart of the matter seems to be the biggest challenge. Looking boldly and openly behind the veil, owning our own personal dilemmas and struggles with racism, facing its manifestations in all their messiness—-this seems to me the first, hardest, and most compelling step. What postmodernism has taught me, what demographic change has proven to me, what simple human decency and civility have viscerally demonstrated for me is that it is in my self-interest to look behind the veil. I do not find it comfortable or easy, and I want time outs and vacations from the task, but it is the task of the times.

Vaclav Havel, discussing his role as a playwright, makes a useful observation in this context. "My ambition is not to soothe the viewer with a merciful lie or cheer him up with a false offer to sort things out for him. I wouldn't be helping him very much if I did. I'm trying to do something else: to propel him, in the most drastic possible way, into the depths of a question he should not, and cannot avoid asking; to stick his nose into his own misery, into my misery, into our common misery, by way of reminding him that the time has come to do something about it (Havel 1990, 199).

Crafting a Preferred Future

I wish I had better news. I also am convinced that my preferred future doesn't give me much choice: I need to mention these things. Advice from others helps me. In 1987, Rushworth Kidder, a columnist for the *Christian Science Monitor*, compiled a collection of interviews with 22 compelling world thinkers, interviews about the 21st century. Mortimer Adler, articulate champion of Western classics, opens the book and observes "I've learned slowly that practical wisdom consists in taking the longest view of things you can" (Adler 1987, 3). This is encouraging, since the long view will no doubt dramatically alter our reading of the Western classics.

Shuichi Kato from Tokyo sounds a first note of counterbalance to our Western ways. "Most people are not very much concerned, seriously, with other people's suffering. By and large it seems to me that the whole of society is geared to domination and manipulation rather than compassion" (Kato 1987, 20). He hopes for something more. Abdus Salam, a Pakistani scientist who is also a Muslim, observes "Everybody seems to be for himself. There is no global vision at all. It's the lack of global vision that worries me, really. It's the issue of globalism that is missing in science, that is missing in the food problem, that is missing in the health problem" (Salam 1987, 113). He asks us to move beyond our national boundaries in ways that make grappling with differences and cultural variance more robust challenges.

Olusegun Obasanjo, Nigeria's former head of state, reflecting on tribalism in African nations, noted that "Over the past twenty-five years there have been internal conflicts in Africa. But no country has really broken in two. In spite of conflicts, they all realize, at the end of the day, the value of living together " (Obasanjo 1987, 174). Our common ground revisits us, the recognition of our interconnectedness. Carlos Fuentes, the Mexican novelist asks "Could we restore a perspective in which values are in conflict, and not good and evil—which is simply melodrama?" (Fuentes 1987, 164). And to conclude this tour of the future, a woman's voice, Sissela Bok, who wants to build a zone of peace for the future, one based on "trust" , where government leaders will need to discover what kinds of actions increase trust. "What that's going to mean, is that officials will have to take moral principles into account—whether or not they really want to" (Bok 1987, 16.)

These voices of a preferred future were of course selected deliberately. They represent some of the more frequently silenced voices in our society, the viewpoints less likely to prevail. And they bring a compelling message about the future, one that, in the long view, involves letting go of manipulation and control, embracing compassion and connectedness. It acknowledges conflict, but invites conflict on values rather than conflict based on labelling persons good or evil. It posits a global worldview and portends constructive outcomes from such global thinking. It acknowledges that we are confronting issues of trust and moral choice.

I like this preferred future. I also find it congruent with the values acknowledged as of importance to nurses and nursing. It fits our stated and unstated codes of conduct. It of course asks of us an honest self-appraisal and a confrontation with the deterrents to the creation of that preferred future. I return to Ueshiba. "Iron is full of impurities that weaken it; through forging, it becomes steel and is transformed into a razor-sharp sword. Human beings develop in the same fashion" (Ueshiba 1992, 56).

Some Letting Go

So the first changes we confront seem to be those that come with forging, with letting go of the "impurities" of nursing education that would merely create appearances. It is no longer enough to tuck a section in a course called "hair care of African Americans" or play a video on the "pregnancy health practices of Latina women." We cannot dismiss our own ignorance nor can we oversimplify our need for learning. We cannot pretend that since we are deeply interested in a culture that is distant and remote, say Nepal or Mongolia, that we have somehow then discharged our difficult duty of multicultural sensitivity, especially if our neighbors and patients are persons we choose to neither know nor understand in a culturally empathic fashion. We cannot pretend that words on paper, clever test questions or proper required readings will achieve goals that can only be achieved through the harrowing process of a change of mind and heart.

We will need to let go of these props and charades and, having peeked behind the veil, then looked long and hard behind the veil, then torn down the veil, extricated ourselves both from the appearances of propriety and the denial of the monster behind the veil. It is not going to be easy, all this letting go.

Beyond the Law

If one wants to have a violent solution to a conflict, one creates a war. If one wants to move toward a more civilized model of conflict resolution, one creates a law. This move from war to civility is best exemplified in this country perusing our legislation on civil rights. While the costly civil war in this country purportedly would solve the issue of slavery and civil rights for "people of color," none of the post war legislation—the 13th, 14th and 15th Amendments in particular—were ever successfully enforced in the confederate states and *de facto* segregation characterized the northern states. Efforts at legislating civil rights was abandoned in 1875 and not revisited until 1957 when two government units were created to secure protection of civil rights. (Bone, 1977).

The 1964 Civil Rights Act, however, changed that. Its major provisions focused on rights about voting, public accommodations, public schools, and private employment. It was followed in 1965 by the Voting Rights Act and in 1968 by the Open Housing Act. This triad of legislative gains were the backdrop and validation of the efforts of Martin Luther King Jr. and the Southern Christian Leadership Conference, among other groups. They, the laws and the demand that their assurances be honored, were the basis for substantive national change. They opened doors and possibilities. They moved us forward.

There is yet a further pathway that we have not yet walked as a nation, a model of conflict resolution that moves beyond rights and legislation and speaks to the heart and mind of the human as human, the common ground of common interests and solutions that benefit us all. The legislation is imperative, and it is not enough. For nurses delivering nursing care, to say at once that they have honored the demands of the law but reserve the right to disdain or even merely misunderstand, by choice, their patients is contrary to our stated values and norms. This modeling of a progression to a more honest resolution of our conflicts is instructive. We can learn from the progress we have made that there is still more work to be done. This is the lesson of the Rodney King beatings, Mark Fuhrman comments, and many like incidents that constitute our daily news.

Once more, Cornel West (1993) says it well. "Our truncated public discussions of race suppress the best of who and what we are as a people because they fail to confront the complexity of the issue in a candid and critical manner" (West 1993, 4). He calls for a revitalized "public conversation about race, in light of our paralyzing pessimism and stultifying cynicism as a people" (West 1993, 158). In analyzing the crisis of black leadership, he aptly describes a leadership deficit that extends to all persons interested in struggling with the matter of race. "We need serious strategic and tactical thinking about how to create new models of leadership and forge the kind of persons to actualize these models" (West 1993, 69). It seems to me that forging these persons, persons of steel in Ueshiba's words, is the challenge to us as nurse educators, and the optimal modeling we can elect to give our students. The law is not enough. We will need more. It will not be easy.

Facing Our Resistances

Jonathan Kozol, in his 1991 analysis of children in America's schools, observes: "There is a deep-seated reverence for fair play in the United States, and in many areas of life we see the consequences in a genuine distaste for loaded dice; but this is not the case in education, health care, or inheritance of wealth. In these elemental areas we want the game to be unfair and we have made it so; and it will likely so remain" (Kozol 1991, 223). In the main, nurse educators do not really address the inheritance of health. But we daily confront two out of three: education and health care. That we, as a society, have made these areas of unfairness and elect to sustain this inequity creates a forceful challenge for nurse educators. We need to know that we really are going to have to rock the boat, and indeed the occupants are not necessarily going to applaud our efforts.

This may be the toughest news of all, for in the end most of us have been educated, trained, rewarded and admired for pleasing people, for creating comfort, for adapting to what is, for accommodating external environments. The challenge of moving beyond appearances to the creation of some preferred future, particularly one beyond the legislated "ought to" and its letter of the law assurances often seems counterintuitive. We are better at healing the wound than we are at being perceived as the person who creates it.

This is an important issue. The killing of messengers is popular sport. The rationalization that others will be so upset that change will simply make them worse becomes a seduction. Despite the fact that the generational "bulge" in our society at this time, the "baby boomers," established themselves as a historical fixture in their dissenting youth, they may not hope now, as they near and pass their fiftieth year of living, to once more be called upon to rock the boat and risk messenger murders. Nonetheless, that is the challenge of the times.

Recalling those same "baby boomers," we can be guided by Abe Fortas who, in 1968 wrote a landmark exploration of dissent and civil disobedience. He eloquently defended the rights of participants, in what he called "the Negro and the youth rebellions" of his times, to dissent. He noted that these groups could not be confined to "polite procedures," asserting that "we can hardly claim that their deserving demands would be satisfied if they did not vigorously assert them" (Fortas 1968, 61). His disclaimer however is that he believed we can "require that the methods which they adopt be within the limits which an organized, democratic society can endure," noting that we must accept the discomforts yet not condone violence or harms to others (Fortas 1968, 62). His distinction is noteworthy. While we elect to not do harm, we will indeed create discomfort. We will no doubt fail to confront issues denied without creating discomfort. Indeed, discomfort may be the indicator that we have succeeded in raising heretofore denied issues to consciousness. We need to be prepared.

Thus, while we may clearly see that both philosophically and pragmatically it is in our self interest to confront "race matters," we can anticipate the resistance that emerges when dissent evokes discomfort. To elect to not act because this discomfort is discomforting is to beg the question. The discomfort and the attendant resistance is to be anticipated, not abhorred. It is the good news. Only then can we begin the tough task of creating new futures in the bright light of an honest recognition of our troublesome dilemmas. And we must honestly begin with our own deep resistances. bell hooks (1990) advises: "Committed cultural critics— whether white or black, scholars or artists—can produce work that opposes structures of domination, that presents possibilities for a transformed future by willingly interrogating their own work on aesthetic and political grounds. This interrogation itself becomes an act of critical intervention, fostering a fundamental attitude of vigilance rather than denial" (hooks 1990, 55).

Coming Full Circle and Getting Practical

I have already discussed in some detail what I believe to be the hard work, the dismantling, the deconstruction of the appearances. It is the step I think we keep missing or avoiding. Suppose we took the step however. Then what? Are there practical things we can do to move us beyond appearances. Intuitively, I believe we will all, each of us, know the answer to that question if we honestly discard the veil of illusion. Nonetheless, in a spirit of pragmatism, some observations may prove useful or catalytic. These are essentially suggestions, things we might elect to do to create our preferred future.

We might ask more questions and give fewer answers. I have found that the only thing I really understand about other cultures is what those intimately involved in those cultures teach me. I am grateful for the lessons, and seek them openly. I find that if I am as authentic as I'm capable of being and come as a student, I learn a great deal. I also seek appraisal of my learning to make sure I am not getting lost in head games or false reassurances. Lessons such as these require respect, commitment and time. We need to make choices.

We might create class exercises or assignments that immerse every student (after we ourselves have embraced the experiment) in a culture other than his or her own. And I do mean immersion, not a dip of the toe in the pond. Such exercises would focus not on facts and trivia but on the lived experience, the phenomenology of this other culture. One only begins to grasp the relativity of culture through systematic and open exposure to other cultures. We would be wise to grant our students the opportunity to learn this as early in life as possible.

We could make race an issue of open dialog and scholarly discourse, teasing apart in a respectful and rigorous fashion the vagaries of racism that shape our lives and the prices we all pay for these daily occurrences. We could struggle toward delineation of common ground, common humanness and its characteristics, shared goals, values and interests. We could require ourselves to explore the implications of "politically correct" behaviors and their potential to build ever more resilient walls of denial.

We could develop, master and teach conflict resolution skills. We already know that the conflicts are in place. We have not yet embraced finding constructive and creative ways to make the conflicts moments of opportunity. It was this that drew me into conflict resolution activities and I have been richly rewarded. We could look at the nature of conflict in health care and begin to understand the power it has in our institutions (Marcus, Dorn, Kritek, Miller, and Wyatt 1995). We could explore the impact of uneven tables and the resultant impact on negotiations toward common interests. This is a particular interest of mind because I find repeatedly that persons who have for decades sat an uneven tables where they were disadvantaged are rarely competent in conflict resolution or positional bargaining skills focused on social justice as a matter of self interest

(Kritek 1994). We have all confused smoothing over conflicts, denial of conflicts, appearances of resolution with actual conflict resolution. The latter is hard work and it is demanding. What we pretend to resolve will merely come back to haunt us as a recurrent conflict process. We and our students need conflict resolution remediation, and we cannot do it too quickly.

We might indeed begin to recraft our curricula so that these various pragmatic options become normative and valued, recognized for their worth in not only improving the capacity of the student to give quality nursing care but also to become a more whole human. We might first manifest the nature of nursing as a healing process by healing ourselves of the blight of racism.

All of these activities would begin to substantively alter the kinds of experiences available to students admitted to our schools, not only those of the dominant culture, but also those of the various "minority" cultures. The disruption alone would serve us all well. And we could learn that we are indeed all in this together, stumbling forward in our humanness but collectively committed to our humaneness.

No Easy Answers

I believe in good questions more than I believe in good answers. I have no panacea, yet believe that honest reflection and careful scholarship unveil that it is indeed in my self-interest to attend to the impact of changing health care systems and changing demographics. I believe that I can acquire the tools to make me a better nurse educator of the future, and I believe in creating a preferred future rather than having it delivered to me for my adaptation to it. I warmly embrace the deeply humanitarian values of the profession of nursing and believe that we are the best equipped group to humanize health care. I believe that all of these are gifts I give my students and that they are of infinite value. Much of what student nurses learn can be mastered through reading and mediated instruction. The changes I describe are of the heart and ask more of me and of my students. I insult them if I give them less. And soberingly, it is in my self-interest and in theirs.

I would like to give Norman Cousins the last word, noting both his ethnicity and his gender as a gesture that reminds me of the importance of finding common ground. His comments conclude his last book, *The Pathology of Power.* In it he analyzes the impact of nuclear weaponry. The analog is worth pondering in the light of other forms of self destruc-tion. He states: ". . . it is precisely because we have to take the world as it is that it becomes necessary to rise above the game if we wish to make our mark. . . .We will succeed only as we represent a rallying center in the world for a less hazardous and more sensible future for all people than is now apparent. Our energies will have a far greater effect if we apply them to the possibilities for human progress rather than to shadowy balance-of-power strategies. . . .Beyond the clamor of clashing ideologies and the preening and jostling of sovereign tribes, a safer and more responsible world is waiting to be created" (Cousins 1987, 208).

References

Adler, M. 1987. Philosopher of Practical Wisdom. In *An Agenda for the 21st Century*, edited by R.M. Kidder. Cambridge, MA: The MIT Press.

Anderson, W.T., ed. 1995. *The Truth About The Truth*. New York: G.P. Putnam's Sons.

Becker, E. 1995. The Fragile Fiction. In *The Truth About the Truth*, edited by W.T. Anderson . New York: G P. Putnam's Sons.

Bok, S. 1987. *Grappling with Principles*. In *An Agenda for the 21st Century*, edited by R.M. Kidder . Cambridge, MA: The MIT Press.

Bone, R.C. 1977. *American Government*. New York: Harper & Row, Publishers, Inc.

Cousins, N. 1987. *The Pathology of Power*. New York: W.W. Norton & Company.

Dock, L.L. 1890. *Textbook on Materia Medica for Nurses*. New York: G.P. Putnam's Sons.

Eisenberg, D.M., R.C. Kessler, C. Foster, F.E. Norlock, D.R. Caulkins, and T.L. Delbanco. 1993. Unconventional medicine in the United States. *The New England Journal of Medicine* 328(4): 246–252.

Fortas, A. 1968. *Concerning Dissent and Civil Disobedience*. New York: Signet Books.

Fuentes, C. 1987. The Gruyere Cheese of Progress. In An Agenda for the 21st Century, edited by R.M. Kidder. Cambridge, MA: The MIT Press.

Gates, Jr., H. L., and C. West. 1996. *The Future of the Race*. New York: Alfred P. Knopf, Inc.

Havel, V. 1990. *Disturbing the Peace*. New York: Vintage Books.

Hooks, B. 1990. *Yearning Race, Gender, and Cultural Politics*. Boston, MA: South End Press.

Kato, S. 1987. Encouraging Compassion. In *An Agenda for the 21st Century*, edited by R.M. Kidder . Cambridge, MA: The MIT Press.

Kidder, R.M. 1987. *An Agenda for the 21st Century*. Cambridge, MA: The MIT Press.

Kozol, J. 1991. *Savage Inequalities*. New York: Crown Publishers, Inc.

Krippner, S., and M. Winkler. 1995. Studying Consciousness in the Postmodern Age. In *The Truth About the Truth*, edited by W.T. Anderson . New York: G.P. Putnam's Sons.

Kritek, P.B. 1994. *Negotiating at an Uneven Table: Developing Moral Courage in Resolving our Conflicts*. San Francisco, CA: Jossey Bass Inc.

Marcus, L. J., B.C. Dorn, P.B. Kritek, V.G. Miller, and J.B. Wyatt. 1995. *Renegotiating Health Care: Resolving Conflict to Build Collaboration*. San Francisco, CA: Jossey-Bass, Inc.

Morganthau, T. 1997. The face of the future. *Newsweek*, January, 58–60.

Nightingale, F. 1969. *Notes on Nursing*. New York: Dover Publications, Inc.

Obasanjo, O. 1987. Waking the Slumbering Giant. In *An Agenda for the 21st Century*, edited by R.M. Kidder. Cambridge, MA: The MIT Press.

Salam, A. 1987. Closing the Great Divide. In *An Agenda for the 21st Century*, edited by R.M. Kidder. Cambridge, MA: The MIT Press.

Simon, W. 1995. *The Postmodernization of Sex and Gender*. In *The Truth About the Truth*, edited by W.T. Anderson. New York: G.P. Putnam's Sons.

Toulmin, S. 1990. *Cosmopolis*. Chicago, IL: The University of Chicago Press.

Ueshiba, M. 1992. *The Art of Peace*. Translated by John Stevens. Boston, MA: Shambhala Publications Inc.

Weisbord, M. R. 1992. *Discovering Common Ground*. San Francisco, CA: Berrett-Koehler Publishers, Inc.

West, C. 1993. *Race Matters*. New York: Vintage Books.

Winslow, R. 1997. Nurses to take doctor duties, Oxford says. *The Wall Street Journal*, February, p. A3.

12

Ingredients Needed for Successful Entry into the Health Profession

*Timothy
Ready,
PhD*

The Association of American Medical Colleges launched *Project 3000 by 2000* in 1991 because it had become apparent that the rapid growth in minority enrollment in medical and other health professions schools that took place in the late 1960s and early 1970s had stalled. Between 1975 and 1990, the rate of increase in the country's Black, Latino and Native American populations substantially out-paced the meager increases in minority enrollment. Despite substantial investments in programs designed to address this issue by the federal government,[1] private foundations and health professions schools, themselves, the problem of minority underrepresentation had become more acute in 1990 than it was 15 years earlier in 1975.

Available data, including surveys of students taking the SAT exam as well as the annual surveys of college freshmen conducted by the Higher Education Research Institute at UCLA, consistently show that the problem of minority underrepresentation in the health professions is not the result of a "lack of interest" in these fields on the part of minority students. Instead, it appears that there is a "disconnect" between minority students' desire to enter the health professions, and their ability to do so. What are the impediments that perpetuate the continued underrepresentation of students from the same racial and ethnic groups that, by law, were denied access to educational and career opportunities throughout most of American history? With support from The U.S. Public Health Service and philanthropies such as the W. K. Kellogg and Robert Wood Johnson Foundations, many health professions schools have devoted considerable resources to minority student recruitment and to educational enrichment

---

[1]These include programs funded by the U.S. Public Health Service, such as the Health Careers Opportunity Program.

programs. Why haven't these programs been able to "solve" the problem of minority underrepresentation?

Students, no matter what their racial/ethic origin, require the same set of *ingredients* if they are to succeed in entering one of the health professions. Historically, and still today, these *ingredients* are far more likely to be available without any outside intervention to non-minority students, especially to those from affluent families. However, these *ingredients* are much less likely to be available to minority and economically disadvantaged students without deliberate efforts to alter the structural barriers and long-standing inequities that continue to restrict educational and career opportunities for this large and growing segment of the U.S. population.

Although the many short-term recruitment and enrichment programs offered by health professions schools have been and continue to be helpful and necessary, they have not been sufficient to fundamentally alter the historical pattern of minority underrepresentation. Such programs may provide students with one or two of the *ingredients* needed for success, but they cannot realistically be expected to provide students with all of them. Each of the following *ingredients* is necessary for successful entry into the health professions but none is sufficient in and of itself. Any successful strategy to improve minority student access to the health professions must systematically work to ensure that students have access to all, beginning no later than the middle school years, onward. Anything short of that is unlikely to substantially increase the number of underrepresented minority students who are able to transform their dreams of becoming a health profession into viable, concrete strategies that will enable them to do so.

Ingredients Needed for Successful Entry into the Health Professions

1. Solid academic preparation prior to college.
2. Access to an undergraduate college with a strong curriculum, taught in an environment supportive of learning and hospitable to students from diverse backgrounds.
3. Experiential learning opportunities in laboratory and clinical settings.
4. Good counseling.
5. Reasonable financial security.
6. Health professions schools and related clinical facilities that are responsible to the needs and interests of the communities they serve.

1. *Solid Academic Preparation Prior to College*

Participation in a rigorous college preparatory curriculum during the high school years is an essential prerequisite to most careers in the health professions, which increasingly require at the very least a bachelor's degree or more, more likely, post-baccalaureate training. Studies from the Department of education show that completion of a demanding sequence of courses is associated with the acquisition of advanced academic skills needed for success in college.

Research conducted for the College Board has demonstrated that completion of algebra no lather than the ninth grade is a strong predictor for completing a sequence of high school courses that will adequately prepare students for college. This sequence of courses should include: four years of mathematics, beginning with algebra no later than the freshman year; four years of English, with a strong emphasis on writing and the reading and interpretation of quality literature that will help students to develop critical thinking skills; a sequence of science courses, including biology, chemistry and physics; and four years of social sciences. Although the gap is narrowing, minority students are still far less likely than others to complete a college preparatory curriculum in high school.

Of course attention to the quality of the curriculum available to minority students must begin much earlier than ninth grade. Students' ability to successfully complete a college curriculum in high school depends, in turn, on the academic preparation students receive during the middle grades.

Data from the Department of Education's National Assessment of Education Progress (NAEP) show that the number of Black, Latino, and other minority students who have developed the skills needed to succeed in college level science courses is alarmingly small. Although there has been improvement over the years in the acquisition of basic skills, the number of minority students who have developed advanced proficiency in mathematics, reading, and writing is distressingly small. Indeed, the number is insufficient to enable enough students to succeed at subsequent stages of the educational pipeline and eventually eliminate the problem of minority underrepresentation in the health professions.

It might be asked, What can nursing, medical, dental, and other health professions schools do to improve the quality of education available to minority students at the precollege level? After all, health professions schools are not primarily responsible for the education of middle school and high school students.

The fact is, health professions skills *can* do a lot, and some already *are* working in partnership with educators based in K–12 school systems to improve educational opportunities and outcomes—especially for minority students who are interested in the health professions. The academic health centers in which most health professions schools are located typically are among the largest, if not THE largest enterprises in their communities. They also are often their communities' largest employers and home to the greatest concentration of scientists and health care providers with advanced training in the sciences. Many are located in or near low income and predominantly minority communities whose schools are especially in need of assistance from their "science rich" neighbors. Given these circumstances, health professions schools have both the means and the responsibility to work in partnership with educators from predominantly minority schools to help eliminate the gaps in educational opportunities and achievements.

2. *Access to an undergraduate college with a strong curriculum, taught in an environment supportive of leaning and hospitable to students from diverse backgrounds.*

To some extent, students' ability to enroll in a high quality institution of higher education is contingent upon developing the prerequisite academic skills in high school, as discussed above. However, many minority students who have the necessary academic skills nevertheless have difficulty enrolling, participating as a full-time student, and graduating from college. Lack of financial resources, a problem that disproportionately affects minority students and their families, is one very important cause that will be further discussed below.

Two other important aspects of this problem that must be considered are the quality of the curricula and the degree to which the campus climate is supportive for students of diverse racial and ethnic backgrounds.

In recent years, the introductory science courses of many colleges have been rightly criticized for being poorly taught. At many, if not most campuses, these courses are primarily responsible for removing many promising students from the health professions education pipeline. Rather than nurturing students' interest and skills in the sciences, many of these courses tend to be exercises in survival and endurance. The Howard Hughes Medical Institute, among others, is working with college science educators to improve the quality of undergraduate science instruction. Of course, the successful completion of these courses depends to a large degree upon the skills students acquire during high school. Nevertheless, encouraging minority students to enroll in colleges that emphasize quality teaching is an important step in addressing minority underrepresentation in the health professions.

The most prestigious colleges and universities do not necessarily provide students with the most supportive environments for learning. Many students of color find that some historically Black and Hispanic serving institutions provide more congenial and supportive learning environments. Historically Black colleges and universities account for a disproportionate share of all bachelor's degrees awarded to Blacks in the sciences. Schools such as Xavier University of Louisiana, Morehouse, Spelman, and Howard have established outstanding records in their regard. For example, Xavier sends nearly twice as many Black students to U.S. medical schools than any other college or university in the country.

In 1996, four of the six leading producers of Black medical students were historically Black colleges and universities.

3. *Experiential leaning opportunities in laboratory and clinical settings*

It is difficult for a student to know whether she or he really wants to become a health professional unless that student has been able to observe first-hand what it is like to be one. Clinical and laboratory internships provide students with a great opportunity to do just that. While such internships can be an important leaning experience for all students, they tend to be especially valuable for minority students, who are much less likely than others to have a close friend or family member who is a health professional.

An internship during high school can help to cement a student's interest in a particular health career, thereby motivating that student to do the hard work that is necessary to achieve his or her career goal. Internships also function to demonstrate to students the relevance of their school work for the careers that interest them. Finally, the interpersonal interaction that students have with mentor health professionals also can be invaluable. Getting to know a medical doctor, nurse, or other health professional as a human being—not just an abstract figure in a white coat—helps the student to visualize himself or herself in that career. Through such internships, health professional mentors can describe the personal problems and challenges that they have had to confront, and also the success strategies that helped them to achieve their career goal. Internships also are a great vehicle for teaching students the values associated with professional service.

4. *Good counseling*

Many students needlessly drop out of the health professions education pipeline due to misinformation that is communicated to them, or because they did not know about existing opportunities and resources. Minority students are less likely than others to have personal networks of family and friends that include health professionals who could provide specific information that is relevant to their career goals. It is crucial that students receive good advice about course selection, the availability of internship and other supplementary learning opportunities, college and health professional school application procedures, and financial aid. Access to counselors who can assist with problems of daily living also is important—especially for students from more disadvantaged backgrounds.

5. *Reasonable financial security*

Too many students of great promise are lost from the health professions educational pipeline because of financial pressures. Minority students, who disproportionately come from low income backgrounds, may feel that they need to work while going to school. Having to work to support oneself, and sometimes other family members, takes away from time that otherwise would be available for study. This can result in lower grades and test scores, lower probability of being accepted to a preferred college, and decreased success to merit-based scholarships—not to mention more fatigue.

The need to work also prevents many students from enrolling in college as full-time students. Part-time study extends the many years of preparation needed to become a health professional even further, and lessens the probability that students will persist until completion of a health professional degree.

6. *Health professions schools and related clinical facilities that are responsive to the needs and interests of the communities they serve*

Unfortunately, it is sometimes the case that health professions schools are geographically located *in* predominantly minority communities but are not *of* those communities. Increasing racial and ethnic diversity in health professions schools requires that faculty, staff, and students of those institutions personally "connect" with prospective minority applicants and the communities from which they come. Needless to say, minority students who perceive that a health professional school is not interested in them or their communities will be unlikely to identify with that school, want to enroll in it, or to even perceive that health profession as an attractive career option.

Because most health professions historically have had few minority practitioners, and minorities continue to be severely underrepresented among the faculty of health professional schools, particular attention must be given to bridging potential communication barriers associated with race and class. The school should embrace service to minority communities as a core component of its mission, and special care may be needed to ensure that members of those communities feel that they are being treated with the same respect, concern, and warmth accorded to others.

13

Exemplary Strategies for the Recruitment, Retention and Graduation of Minorities in Nursing

Hattie Bessent,
EdD, RN, FAAN

Introduction

The underrepresentation of minorities in the health professions is a genuine concern for the nation considering the changing health care system and the implications for the nation's workforce. As the demographics change there is a growing realization that our nation will not be able to thrive in the twenty-first century without a willingness to recognize, stimulate and develop the capacities of all segments of society and to acknowledge the needs of these groups currently underrepresented in health careers (Lewin and Rice 1994).

There is a belief that institutions of higher education can play a definitive role in increasing ethnic and racial diversity in society. Almost all campuses now see education of a diverse citizenry as integral to their missions of public leadership and service (AACU 1995). An examination of how to assure the inclusion of more African Americans, Hispanics, Asians and Native Americans in nursing is presented from a varied prospective in chapters preceding this one.

Successful means of attracting, retaining and graduating minority students for nursing degree programs is a complex, involved undertaking. This chapter includes, what I have described as, exemplary strategies to recruit, retain and graduate minority students from baccalaureate and graduate degree programs in nursing.

It is evident that there are overlaps and interrelationships among the programs. They do, however, represent what some believe are illustrative for success in recruiting, retaining and graduating minority students. Multiple sources were used to identify the strategies. These sources are described in Chapter 1. A group of experts identified and agreed to the strategies that are included. A panel of ten experts and ten former fellows of the American Nurses Association Minority Fellows program ranked the strategies with one being the highest and most important. The rankings of the experts and fellows of the strategies are in Appendix 3. Presentation of the strategies have been addressed using some information obtained from students enrolled in ten university nursing programs who participated in focus groups and information from various other sources (e.g. experts, faculty, administrators, etc.). These strategies and the content of the preceding chapters provide a framework for viewing nursing in a broader context than that delineated in the Institute of Medicine Study on ensuring racial and ethnic diversity in the health profession.

The strategies may be used to facilitate ethnic diversity in institutions of higher education. Innovative ways to use, test and improve them are encouraged. Specific assumptions, beliefs and values have shaped the paradigm in which the strategies are presented. The most fundamental assumption or belief is that the administrators, faculty and staff of nursing programs in institutions of higher learning can customize the strategies presented in each of the functions for their own settings. Some of the strategies may be useful in more than one of the functions. They are viewed as future oriented because they are flexible, and the investigator hopes, responsive to the realities that the profession of nursing faces in terms of enhancing ethnic and racial diversity.

Recruitment

A. The University/College/School of Nursing interested in recruiting minorities (African Americans, Asians, Latinos (Hispanics), and/or Native Americans) should:

1. See that the recruitment of nursing students is part of the University's effort and involves the administrator responsible for students, admissions, registration and other pertinent entities on the campus.

2. Develop packages which provide information on admission criteria, standardized test scores, requirements for graduation, financial aid, housing, student health, student fees (e.g., for computers, activities, and laboratories), support services (e.g., counseling, child care, writing and speaking laboratories, and tutorial assistance).

3. Market nursing better and assure that the information about nursing is provided to inform the public and particularly to assist high school counselors.

4. Assure that the nature of nursing and its options for career development are better presented.

5. Orient recruiters so that they not only have an understanding of the nursing program but an understanding of the expectations of

the University (e.g., general education requirements, assessing support services, etc.)

6. Be aware of different learning styles of students and have ways of assessing how best to help students admitted to the program be successful.

B. The recruiter of minority students for programs in nursing should:

1. Represent the same minority background as the individual(s) being recruited or have some connection with the community from which the student is being recruited.

2. Collaborate with the community of the targeted population from which the individual(s) are being recruited to secure resolution from and endorsement of the community.

3. Be aware of family influence on the prospective recruit(s) and recognize the nature of the impact on the family of the recruit being enrolled in a nursing program in an institutional setting.

4. Elicit the help of an advisory group composed of representatives of a targeted population from which the individual(s) are being recruited.

5. Recognize the perception of family and recruit about the profession of nursing and be prepared to discuss the length of the program, the types of programs, the varied opportunities nursing presents and the potential growth in the discipline.

Recruitment

Marketing and the communication of information are operative words for any successful recruitment program in nursing. The commitment of the university to diversity appears to be a key ingredient in marketing and supporting schools and colleges of nursing that have strategies and methods for recruiting minority students. The survey that was done revealed that all of the institutions that provided responses have strategies and methods for recruiting minority students. University administrators have accepted the "pool problem" in terms of the recruitment of graduate students, according to a report of the American Council on Higher Education. A frequent reason given for the limited size of the pool of graduate school applicants of color is the view that "market forces" operate to drive talented students of color into professional fields such as law, medicine and business (Knowles and Harleston 1997). This nation, based on government, several foundations and professional organizations, seems to support the view that there are multiple options for minority students. Consequently packaging information becomes very important in the recruitment process both for undergraduate and graduate students.

Packaging information must be effective if any attention is to be given to it. Each of the strategies for the recruitment function include an aspect of marketing and communication of information. The provision of oral as well as written information is ideal. Sims identified ways to revitalize recruitment communication. Among her ideas were to develop a fresh theme and identify what is really distinctive about the school(Sims 1997, 2). Helping perspective students understand what is distinctive about the nursing program and what roles they may assume when they complete the program may also be an attraction. The provision of eye catching follow-up publications on such subjects as financial aid and educational outcomes with repeated, reinforced and reiterated key messages was also seen as important in packaging recruitment information. Knowing something about students that you wish to recruit is very important. This will help in targeting messages more appropriately. One should know what the racial, ethnic and cultural backgrounds are of the students that are being targeted. Are the students in elementary school, high school or are they adults in particular roles in nursing (e.g., licensed practical nurses, diploma or associate degree graduates)? The communication flow is likely to be different depending on who is being targeted. The messages to elementary school students will certainly be different from high school students and the messages for high school students different from adults who may have, for example, an associate degree in nursing. What are the needs of the individual students being recruited? Do they have young children? Are there day care facilities on the campus they can use? Knowing something about the student being recruited is a strategically positive indicator as to whether the student will likely enter the program and be successful in it. Family influence and collaboration with the community of the targeted population were also seen as important by experts, fellows and students.

Many of the students in the focus group indicated that the location and reputation of the school and program were important to them. The curriculum content offered in the program was an important consideration to students in the focus groups. Few students in the focus group mentioned learning styles directly. This, however, was identified by experts as an important consideration in recruiting and retaining students. Most members of the focus groups indicated that they selected the school they attended based on two factors—location and reputation of the program.

Several of the students in the focus groups thought the recruiter should represent the same minority background as the individuals being recruited. Fellows ranked this strategy second and experts ranked it last in terms of importance. Some students in focus groups felt that former graduates, faculty and high school counselors should recruit new students. They also felt that there should be something about careers available for all students in high school, that counselors should be involved and students encouraged to attend career days. There were numerous statements about what nursing recruiters don't do. Among them were financial aid, which is a difficult subject, is not explained and the brochures on financial aid are not available before the recruiters come. Consequently, there is not an opportunity to get information needed from the recruiters on financial aid. Financial security in the form of financial aid and scholarships and whether the program is affordable were identified as important by students in the focus groups. Some recruiters were said to be not very knowledgeable about the university and have limited information about the nursing school. The issue of remediation appears to be addressed in summer programs. If summer developmental programs are offered to help students entering nursing programs, students in the focus groups felt they should be of a length (e.g., at least two months) that allows students to begin with other nursing students when school starts in the fall. It seems important to students in focus groups that recruiters provide information and that students who need development programs be allowed to begin with other students in the fall.

Advisory groups of representatives in the community may be one of the ways to bridge the gap between the formal recruiter and students interested in programs. Every opportunity to present nursing as an attractive career should be made. Nurses associations such as the Jamaican, Black, Hispanic, Asian and Pacific Islanders, Indians and others in the community such as alumni associations and individual alumni were identified by fellows, experts, and students as potential sources to help with recruitment and retention of minority students. Coalitions and partnerships have been encouraged. The Minority Nurse Congress, sponsored by the Division of Nursing, have made recommendations for increasing the number of well prepared minority nurses, too. Proper advisement seems to be another important dimension that cannot be stressed too often.

The importance of recognizing the background of targeted populations or individuals is very important. Are they undergraduate or graduate students? Some differences will likely be needed in how students are approached based on their level of education. Cultural differences and ethnicity are important to consider in recruiting students. Individuals may have the same cultural backgrounds but be of different racial groups. For example, there are Hispanics who could be classified based on physical features as Caucasian and some who based on their physical features would be classified racially as Black. Individuals may be of the same race but of different ethnic groups. (e.g., Hispanic Mexicans, Puerto Ricans, Cubans,). Individuals may be of different races but of the same ethnic group (e.g., White Catholics, Hispanic Catholics and Black Catholics). Recognizing that minorities are not a monolithic group of individuals is extremely important. During the focus group, several participants pointed out that all minorities do not come from poor families and that all are not educationally disadvantaged. It was also noted that the actions of institutions are more persuasive than words. Some schools say that they support diversity and want to recruit, enroll and retain minorities. However, they have few or no minorities in any roles in the school.

Retention

A. The institution has a positive valuation of multiculturalism and this is demonstrated in the following ways:

1. Provides administrative support of cultural diversity in the faculty and students.

2. Allocates resources to further the initiatives that assure support of cultural diversity.

3. Requires a systematic and periodic evaluation of programs offered by the University and an aspect of that evaluation considers diversity of faculty and students.

4. Recognizes the importance of cultural enrichment in programs and considers the moral, political, economic and global dimensions.

5. Builds multiple strategies and means to facilitate minority faculty and student success.

B. The nursing program administration:

1. Creates an environment of open communication.

2. Commits to leadership development of minority students along with other students enrolled in the program.

3. Utilizes variance in measuring achievement and is sensitive to cultural variance.

4. Has clear expectations of students and delineates them to students who are admitted to the program.

5. Provides the administrative support that will enable a student to succeed.

6. Provides both internal and external mentors for students.

7. Helps faculty and staff recognize and acknowledge the value and influence of family for many minority groups.

8. Balance flexible accommodation of special circumstances with cultivation of professional norms and standards.

9. Capitalize on and provide existing technological tools (e.g., distance learning, learning modules, computer aided instruction) to maximize alternative learning opportunities.

C. The faculty of the nursing program:

1. Admits only those students the faculty believes will be able to succeed.

2. Provides means to help students understand the curriculum and what is expected through effective communication, collaboration and group skills.

3. Provides counseling and advising for anticipated student needs.

4. Helps students with negotiating skills and how to access available resources.

5. Helps students learn effective use of assertiveness skills.

6. Coordinates mentoring and assures that the process of linking students with people who can assist them is effective.

7. Helps students learn to resolve conflict.

8. Provide students with skills to adopt to the institutional culture without losing their own identity.

Retention

The operative word in retention is support. Climate and resources appear to be two of the critical factors in support. The success of students who enroll in a program is dependent upon the support they receive to a great extent. In reviewing the written and verbal responses of students who participated in focus groups many of the responses seem to indicate that students need some sort of supportive relationship when going through their programs. This is especially true in their relationships with teachers and advisors. Students who are successful also seem to need support to feel comfortable in the educational environment. Social acceptance, as a worthwhile student by other students, staff and faculty, was identified as important to students in the focus groups. Good relationships with other students, whether they be more experienced or peers, were specifically noted in focus groups. Students mentioned things such as "constant encouragement", "guidance", "caring helpful attitude", "understanding and caring staff", etc.

Some students gave examples of what they felt was helpful in terms of a supportive climate. "Staff and faculty value our grievances and help is available. They are open to improvement." "The Minority Affairs Director is available night or day if you have a concern." "All faculty seem to move with you as you move through the programs. They remember your name, stop you in the corridor and check on how you are doing. If you need help they see that you get it."

Creative approaches to improve the climate for minority students may enhance the climate for all students. The approaches may be another means of recognizing what students in your institution need to be successful. Chang found that having a diverse student body is associated with several attributes of the institutional climate. Among them were stronger commitment to multiculturalism, more frequent student involvement in cultural awareness workshops and ethnic study courses (Chang 1996). A positive impact seems to result from socializing across racial lines and participating in discussion of racial issues. These seem to contribute to or have a positive impact on student retention, overall college satisfaction, intellectual self-confidence and social self-confidence according to Astin (Astin 1993).

Climates that are culturally competent (one that actively seeks the participation of those who have a different cultural background) or culturally proficient, (one that holds cultural differences in high esteem) are seen as supportive. Those climates that are culturally destructive (one in which the culture is seen as inferior or distasteful to that of the dominant culture) or culturally blind (one that does not see or accept any differences) are viewed as non-supportive.

The nature of the learner and learning styles are important dimensions to consider when recruiting, enrolling and retaining students in programs. Teaching methods other than the traditional ones, such as problem based learning, are being used to help students learn. Students in focus groups responded positively to culture content being in the curriculum. Inclusion of cultural content in the curriculum may be one approach to enhance the climate for all students and assure that culture is respected.

Student organizations, tutors, minority affairs offices and mentors were some of the resources that were identified most along with financial aid. Financial support for both undergraduate and graduate students may come from a variety of sources. Students who have solid academic achievement should be able to access help with finances if they need them. Students who complete high caliber undergraduate programs should be able to get support for graduate programs in the form of fellowships, teaching assistants and research assistants.

Graduation

A. The following are essential environmental elements that exist in the institution for students to successfully matriculate and graduate:

1. There must be resocialization of the faculty to create a successful oriented milieu.

2. There must be interaction and communication between majority and minority students and faculty.

3. Every effort must be made to eliminate cognitive dissonance between majority and minority individuals and the creation of psychological and physical comfort between the individuals.

4. Every effort must be made to select deans, chairs and faculty who have the capacity to respect and empower others and who possess self-esteem and value the contributions of others.

B. An institution which facilitates and promotes graduation has the following implements on behalf of its students:

1. It enhances student socialization in that it values people.

2. It connects the student with resources (financial, library, computers, writing assistance, speaking assistance, advisors, models of successful people, participation in work with successful faculty, study groups and tutors).

3. It provides intellectual stimulation for students.

4. It sets forth indicators of the acquisition of knowledge for students.

5. It provides supplemental opportunities for the enhancement of student learning if warranted (e.g., additional clinical activity).

C. An institution that is committed to students being productive has these environmental elements:

1. It clearly identifies the value of people as intellectual, economic, social and moral capital.

2. It recognizes that the failure to promote and graduate students results in serious casualties such as individuals who are dysfunctional, frozen in careers, or who are subject to rage and consequently immobilization of talent.

3. It creates a desire for an emphasizes principles of justice, ethics, and intellectual honesty.

4. It transmits the joy of learning and a thirst for new knowledge.

5. It establishes a contractual relationship between the student and the faculty member in which the roles of student and faculty are clearly delineated and understood.

Graduation

Mentoring and advisement are essential elements in a student's progression toward graduation. An intellectually stimulating program and rewarding educational experience is what institutions of higher learning should aspire to for all of their graduates. A key element for graduates is that they have had an intellectually stimulating program that prepares

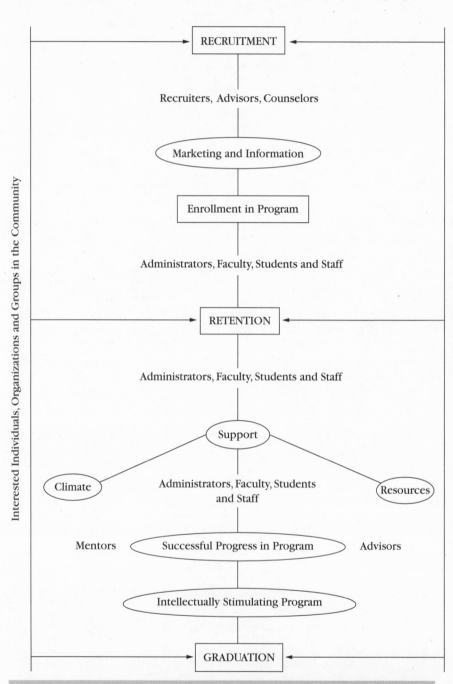

Figure 1. Exemplary Strategies to Recruit, Retain and Graduate Minority Students In Nursing

them to succeed in a rapidly changing world. Students should be nurtured, respected and provided the opportunity to enjoy their educational achievements regardless of their ethnic, racial or cultural background.

Undergraduate education in nursing and graduate education should focus on the needs of society. There is ample evidence that baccalaureate, master's and doctoral prepared minority nurses are needed to assume roles in a wide array of settings. Experiential learning experiences are desirable for both undergraduate and graduate students. It is not enough for institutions to educate future leaders of various minority groups, but to educate them in an environment where they and other students learn from and about each other.

Summary

It is my belief that many of the administrators in higher education institutions and in nursing programs support diversity and recognize that our society is becoming more diverse and that the economy of the United States is influenced more by global factors. However, they have not been effective in convincing those who work in the institution that diversity in terms of the students, faculty and the curriculum need to be implemented to prepare all of the students for the transformations that are taking place in society.

The strategies presented in this chapter are illustrations of means that can mean dynamic results for institutions when considering the issue of recruiting, retaining and graduating minority students. Figure one highlights the basic elements or operative words for each of the functions. A combination of elements are inherent in the processes that are necessary for a student to enter and graduate from a program. The importance of ensuring dignity for all students who enter the portals of educational programs in our universities is a goal that is positive for the nation as well as the student. It is no longer in the interest of the nation or any of its institutions to marginalize or exclude minorities from fully participating and contributing to the nation.

References

Association of American Colleges and Universities (AACU). 1995. *The Drama of Diversity and Democracy: Higher Education and American Commitments*. Washington, DC: Association of American Colleges and Universities.

Astin, A. 1993. Diversity and Multiculturalism on Campus: How are Students Affected? *Change* (March/April).

Chang, M. 1996. Racial Diversity in Higher Education: Does a Racially Mixed Student Population Affect Education Outcomes. Unpublished Doctoral Dissertation. Los Angeles, CA.

Knowles, M. F., and B.W. Harleston. 1997. *Achieving Diversity in the Professoriate: Challenges and Opportunities. A Report for the American Council on Education.* Washington, DC: American Council on Education.

Lewin, M, and B. Rice, eds. 1994. *Balancing the scales of opportunity in health care: Ensuring racial and ethnic diversity in the health professions.* Washington, DC: National Academy Press.

Sims, Ruth. 1997. Ten Ways to Revitalize Your Recruitment Communication Strategies. Strategies. Iowa City: USA Group Noel-Levitz.

Survey Instrument

Recruitment, Retention and Graduation of Minorities Questionnaire

Instructions:

This survey should take about thirty minutes to complete. The information you provide will be treated as confidential and will be used for statistical purposes in the development of a framework for achieving ethnic diversity in nursing. Information will be placed in the form of statistical summaries from which it will be impossible to identify any specific person or institution. Your response is entirely voluntary and failure to provide some or all of the requested information will in no way affect you adversely.

Part 1. General Information

A. The total number of students by sex enrolled in the nursing programs identified below. (Complete all that apply)

	Male	Female	Total	
1				Undergraduate
2				Master's
3				Doctoral
4				Other (e.g., specialist, certification etc. Please specify)

B. The total number of minority students by sex enrolled in the nursing programs identified below

	African-American		Asian		Hispanic		Native American	
	M	F	M	F	M	F	M	F
Undergraduate								
Master's								
Doctoral								
Other (Please specify)								

C. The total number of students by sex who graduated in the last five years.
(Complete all that apply)

	Male	Female	Total	
1				Undergraduate
2				Master's
3		.		Doctoral
4				Other (e.g., specialist, certification etc. Please specify)

D. The total number of minorities by sex that graduated in the last five years.

	African-American		Asian		Hispanic		Native American	
	M	F	M	F	M	F	M	F
Undergraduate								
Master's								
Doctoral								
Other (Please specify)								

Part II. Recruitment

A. Does your college/school have methods and/or strategies for recruiting minority students?
_____Yes   _____ No
On a scale of 1 to 10, how important are these strategies?
Not at all important 0   1   2   3   4   5   6   7   8   9   10 very important

B. Describe your college/school's methods and/or strategies for recruiting minority students. (If you have a brochure or specific statement on such recruitment, please attach to Questionnaire.)

_____

_____

_____

_____

_____

_____

_____

C. How effective are the strategies and/or methods your college/school uses in recruiting students?

Not at all effective <u>0   1   2   3   4   5   6   7   8   9   10</u> very effective

D. If not, why not?

_____

_____

_____

_____

_____

_____

_____

_____

E. If yes, rank order of the strategies or methods that are the most effective beginning with the most effective to the least effective.

_____

_____

_____

_____

_____

_____

F. Identify specific barriers that prevent your college/school from actively recruiting minorities:

_____

_____

_____

_____

_____

_____

Part III. Retention

A. Rank order of the barriers in retaining minority students in your program(s) from most difficult to least difficult.

_____

_____

_____

_____

_____

_____

B. Rank order of the strategies/methods that are most effective in retaining minority students in your program(s) from most effective to least effective.

_____

_____

_____

_____

_____

_____

C. Are the strategies different for the level of students?

Undergraduate   _____ Yes   _____ No

Master's   _____ Yes   _____ No

Doctoral   _____ Yes   _____ No

Other (e.g. specialist certificate.   _____ Yes   _____ No
Please specify)

D. If you answered yes to any of the above sections in Item C, please indicate the difference.

_____

_____

_____

_____

_____

_____

PART IV. *Activities to Enhance Recruitment, Retention and Graduation*

A. Rank order of activities that are used to enhance recruitment, retention and graduation of minority students from most important to least important.

_____

_____

_____

_____

_____

_____

B. Do you have minority faculty?

_____ Yes   _____ No

If so, how many? _____

C. Rank order of activities that are used to assist your majority faculty in enhancing the potential success with minority students in the retention, recruitment and graduation from the most effective activities to the least effective activities.

_____

_____

_____

_____

_____

_____

D. Rank order of activities of the minority faculty that may enhance the potential success with minority students in the retention, recruitment and graduation from most effective activity to least effective activity.

_____

_____

_____

_____

_____

_____

E. If you have any comments about recruitment, retention and graduation of minority students, please share them with me.

_____

_____

_____

_____

_____

_____

APPENDIX 2

Tables

Part I: General Information

Table 1A(1) List of Mean and Median Responses to Part 1
Question A: Enrollments

Variable	N	Mean	Std Dev	Median	Q1	Q3
Male Und	32	43.5	33.4	37.5	18.5	62.5
Female Und	32	333.8	207.6	287.5	204.5	454.0
Total Und	32	377.3	231.3	328.5	231.0	529.5
Male Masters	32	21.5	48.2	11.5	7.5	20.5
Female Masters	32	205.2	106.5	197.0	143.0	262.5
Total Masters	32	226.8	105.9	209.0	158.5	281.5
Male Doctoral	32	2.3	3.2	1.5	1.0	3.0
Female Doctoral	32	49.4	36.2	41.0	24.0	70.0
Total Doctoral	32	51.8	38.7	43.5	25.5	71.0
Male Other	32	1.3	3.8	0.0	0.0	0.5
Female Other	32	18.1	36.7	0.0	0.0	14.5
Total Other	32	19.4	39.8	0.0	0.0	15.5
Male Total	32	68.7	55.9	56.5	36.0	79.5
Female Total	32	606.5	276.8	585.0	441.0	774.5
Total Enrolled	32	675.2	297.1	672.5	486.5	862.5

Table 1A(2) List of Mean and Median Responses to Part 1
Question A: Enrollments
Eliminate Responders not Offering Degree

Variable	N	Mean	Std Dev	Median	Q1	Q3
Male Und	29	48.0	31.8	42.0	26.0	66.0
Female Und	29	368.3	185.9	362.0	237.0	459.0
Total Und	29	416.3	205.9	424.0	270.0	530.0
Male Masters	31	22.2	48.8	12.0	8.0	21.0
Female Masters	31	211.8	101.4	199.0	148.0	265.0
Total Masters	31	234.1	99.1	211.0	160.0	285.0
Male Doctoral	31	2.4	3.3	2.0	1.0	3.0
Female Doctoral	31	51.0	35.6	43.0	25.0	70.0
Total Doctoral	31	53.4	38.1	45.0	27.0	71.0
Male Other	11	3.8	5.8	1.0	0.0	6.0
Female Other	11	52.5	46.6	33.0	14.0	99.0
Total Other	11	56.4	51.2	34.0	15.0	108.0
Male Total	32	68.7	55.9	56.5	36.0	79.5
Female Total	32	606.5	276.8	585.0	441.0	774.5
Total Enrolled	32	675.2	297.1	672.5	486.5	862.5

Table 1B(1) List of Mean and Median Responses to Part 1, Question B
African American Enrollments
(Frequency Count)
Eliminate Responders not Offering Degree

Variable	N	Mean	Std Dev	Median	Q1	Q3
Male Und	27	2.78	3.42	2.00	0.00	4.00
Female Und	27	26.52	28.54	16.00	9.00	36.00
Total Und	29	30.59	31.54	18.00	11.00	41.00
Male Masters	29	0.45	0.69	0.00	0.00	1.00
Female Masters	29	8.52	8.21	6.00	2.00	14.00
Total Masters	31	9.06	8.59	7.00	2.00	16.00
Male Doctoral	29	0.10	0.31	0.00	0.00	0.00
Female Doctoral	29	3.03	3.39	2.00	0.00	5.00
Total Doctoral	31	3.06	3.42	2.00	0.00	6.00
Male Other	11	0.18	0.40	0.00	0.00	0.00
Female Other	11	3.18	5.84	1.00	0.00	4.00
Total Other	11	3.36	5.85	1.00	0.00	4.00
Male Total	30	3.10	3.73	2.00	0.00	4.00
Female Total	30	36.20	36.28	25.00	12.00	51.00
Total Enrolled	30	39.30	39.38	27.00	12.00	51.00

Table 1B(2) List of Mean and Median Responses to Part 1, Question B
African American Enrollments
(Relative Frequency %)
Eliminate Responders not Offering Degree

Variable	N	Mean	Std Dev	Median	Q1	Q3
Male Und	27	5.31	5.43	4.44	0.00	8.33
Female Und	27	7.02	4.90	6.45	3.19	10.14
Total Und	29	6.90	4.48	6.64	3.80	9.51
Male Masters	29	2.75	4.16	0.00	0.00	4.76
Female Masters	29	4.27	4.47	3.52	1.25	6.02
Total Masters	31	3.52	2.65	2.67	1.18	6.24
Male Doctoral	23	6.28	21.67	0.00	0.00	0.00
Female Doctoral	29	6.04	8.09	5.26	0.00	8.47
Total Doctoral	31	6.03	8.54	5.15	0.00	8.89
Male Other	8	2.05	4.10	0.00	0.00	2.63
Female Other	11	4.06	4.92	3.85	0.00	6.67
Total Other	11	4.02	4.66	3.85	0.00	6.67
Male Total	30	4.25	4.05	3.18	0.00	6.45
Female Total	30	5.47	3.73	5.13	2.64	7.29
Total Enrolled	30	5.30	3.63	4.74	2.88	6.98

Table 1B(3) List of Mean and Median Responses to Part 1, Question B
Asian Enrollments
(Frequency Count)
Eliminate Responders not Offering Degree

Variable	N	Mean	Std Dev	Median	Q1	Q3
Male Und	27	1.89	1.97	1.00	1.00	3.00
Female Und	27	16.04	11.98	14.00	9.00	16.00
Total Und	29	17.79	12.07	15.00	10.00	19.00
Male Masters	29	0.55	1.12	0.00	0.00	1.00
Female Masters	29	7.72	11.05	5.00	1.00	9.00
Total Masters	31	7.77	11.62	5.00	1.00	9.00
Male Doctoral	29	0.10	0.31	0.00	0.00	0.00
Female Doctoral	29	2.55	4.52	1.00	0.00	2.00
Total Doctoral	31	2.52	4.60	1.00	0.00	2.00
Male Other	11	0.09	0.30	0.00	0.00	0.00
Female Other	11	1.45	2.62	1.00	0.00	2.00
Total Other	11	1.55	2.62	1.00	0.00	2.00
Male Total	30	2.37	1.97	2.00	1.00	3.00
Female Total	30	24.90	19.20	19.50	11.00	35.00
Total Entrolled	30	27.27	19.81	22.00	13.00	37.00

Table 1B(4) List of Mean and Median Responses to Part 1, Question B
Asian Enrollments
(Relative Frequency %)
Eliminate Responders not Offering Degree

Variable	N	Mean	Std Dev	Median	Q1	Q3
Male Und	27	5.28	6.72	3.03	1.69	7.69
Female Und	27	6.79	10.76	4.63	2.16	7.43
Total Und	29	6.41	9.97	4.13	2.68	6.77
Male Masters	29	3.22	6.08	0.00	0.00	4.76
Female Masters	29	4.68	9.02	2.39	0.99	3.70
Total Masters	31	2.97	4.14	2.17	0.79	3.33
Male Doctoral	23	9.18	28.75	0.00	0.00	0.00
Female Doctoral	29	5.64	7.66	3.23	0.00	5.71
Total Doctoral	31	5.11	7.22	2.82	0.00	5.56
Male Other	8	1.39	3.93	0.00	0.00	0.00
Female Other	11	2.18	2.79	1.01	0.00	5.00
Total Other	11	2.14	2.59	1.53	0.00	4.76
Male Total	30	4.42	4.68	2.99	1.99	6.02
Female Total	30	4.61	4.70	3.51	2.20	5.64
Total Entrolled	30	4.54	4.63	3.12	2.23	5.30

Table 1B(5) List of Mean and Median Responses to Part 1, Question B
Hispanic Enrollments
(Frequency Count)
Eliminate Responders not Offering Degree

Variable	N	Mean	Std Dev	Median	Q1	Q3
Male Und	27	2.04	4.61	1.00	0.00	2.00
Female Und	27	9.81	12.94	5.00	4.00	14.00
Total Und	29	11.21	16.87	5.00	4.00	14.00
Male Masters	29	0.41	0.73	0.00	0.00	1.00
Female Masters	29	4.90	7.68	2.00	0.00	5.00
Total Masters	31	5.00	8.01	2.00	0.00	5.00
Male Doctoral	29	0.07	0.26	0.00	0.00	0.00
Female Doctoral	29	1.03	1.68	0.00	0.00	2.00
Total Doctoral	31	1.03	1.78	0.00	0.00	2.00
Male Other	11	0.00	0.00	0.00	0.00	0.00
Female Other	11	0.64	1.03	0.00	0.00	1.00
Total Other	11	0.64	1.03	0.00	0.00	1.00
Male Total	30	2.30	4.53	1.00	1.00	2.00
Female Total	30	14.80	18.15	10.00	5.00	20.00
Total Enrolled	30	17.10	22.33	10.50	6.00	22.00

Table 1B(6) List of Mean and Median Responses to Part 1, Question B
Hispanic Enrollments
(Relative Frequency %)
Eliminate Responders not Offering Degree

Variable	N	Mean	Std Dev	Median	Q1	Q3
Male Und	27	5.13	8.29	2.38	0.00	4.44
Female Und	27	3.38	4.11	1.44	0.96	4.46
Total Und	29	3.37	4.28	1.42	0.85	4.00
Male Masters	29	2.84	6.16	0.00	0.00	4.55
Female Masters	29	3.04	6.28	1.12	0.00	2.02
Total Masters	31	1.92	3.11	1.08	0.00	1.75
Male Doctoral	23	2.66	10.58	0.00	0.00	0.00
Female Doctoral	29	2.54	6.51	0.00	0.00	2.22
Total Doctoral	31	2.32	5.88	0.00	0.00	2.82
Male Other	8	0.00	0.00	0.00	0.00	0.00
Female Other	11	0.91	1.58	0.00	0.00	1.60
Total Other	11	0.84	1.49	0.00	0.00	1.53
Male Total	30	4.18	6.78	1.76	0.32	4.17
Female Total	30	2.85	3.56	1.62	0.74	3.61
Total Enrolled	30	2.90	3.74	1.59	0.82	3.26

Table 1B(7) List of Mean and Median Responses to Part 1, Question B
Native American Enrollments
(Frequency Count)
Eliminate Responders not Offering Degree

Variable	N	Mean	Std Dev	Median	Q1	Q3
Male Und	27	0.33	0.68	0.00	0.00	1.00
Female Und	27	2.04	2.59	2.00	0.00	3.00
Total Und	29	2.28	2.86	2.00	0.00	3.00
Male Masters	29	0.21	0.77	0.00	0.00	0.00
Female Masters	29	5.62	25.12	1.00	0.00	2.00
Total Masters	31	5.48	25.01	1.00	0.00	2.00
Male Doctoral	29	0.03	0.19	0.00	0.00	0.00
Female Doctoral	29	0.24	0.51	0.00	0.00	0.00
Total Doctoral	31	0.26	0.58	0.00	0.00	0.00
Male Other	11	0.00	0.00	0.00	0.00	0.00
Female Other	11	0.45	0.82	0.00	0.00	1.00
Total Other	11	0.45	0.82	0.00	0.00	1.00
Male Total	30	0.53	1.17	0.00	0.00	1.00
Female Total	30	7.67	26.30	2.00	1.00	4.00
Total Enrolled	30	8.20	27.17	2.50	1.00	4.00

Table 1B(8) List of Mean and Median Responses to Part 1, Question B
Native American Enrollments
(Relative Frequency %)
Eliminate Responders not Offering Degree

Variable	N	Mean	Std Dev	Median	Q1	Q3
Male Und	27	1.78	6.42	0.00	0.00	1.32
Female Und	27	1.74	6.17	0.32	0.00	0.84
Total Und	29	1.63	5.97	0.27	0.00	0.67
Male Masters	29	1.69	7.46	0.00	0.00	0.00
Female Masters	29	3.00	11.66	0.19	0.00	0.54
Total Master	31	2.31	10.88	0.33	0.00	0.50
Male Doctoral	23	4.35	20.85	0.00	0.00	0.00
Female Doctoral	29	0.50	1.18	0.00	0.00	0.00
Total Doctoral	31	0.56	1.47	0.00	0.00	0.00
Male Other	8	0.00	0.00	0.00	0.00	0.00
Female Other	11	0.44	0.78	0.00	0.00	1.28
Total Other	11	0.41	0.71	0.00	0.00	1.28
Male Total	30	1.55	6.49	0.00	0.00	0.79
Female Total	30	2.35	10.06	0.34	0.17	0.80
Total Enrolled	30	2.29	9.88	0.33	0.21	0.74

Table 1B(9) List of Mean and Median Responses to Part 1, Question B
Total Minorities Enrollments
(Frequency Count)
Eliminate Responders not Offering Degree

Variable	N	Mean	Std Dev	Median	Q1	Q3
Male Und	27	7.04	8.52	5.00	3.00	7.00
Female Und	27	54.41	38.87	42.00	31.00	74.00
Total Und	29	61.86	44.41	45.00	34.00	80.00
Male Masters	29	1.62	2.38	1.00	0.00	2.00
Female Masters	29	26.76	41.43	18.00	4.00	29.00
Total Masters	31	27.32	42.28	20.00	4.00	29.00
Male Doctoral	29	0.31	0.66	0.00	0.00	0.00
Female Doctoral	29	6.86	7.89	4.00	2.00	8.00
Total Doctoral	31	6.87	8.16	4.00	2.00	8.00
Male Other	11	0.27	0.65	0.00	0.00	0.00
Female Other	11	5.73	8.16	3.00	0.00	6.00
Total Other	11	6.00	8.33	3.00	0.00	7.00
Male Total	30	8.30	8.69	6.00	4.00	9.00
Female Total	30	83.57	63.96	65.50	33.00	124.00
Total Enrolled	32	91.25	68.48	71.00	35.50	132.50

Table 1B(10) List of Mean and Median Responses to Part 1, Question B
Total Minorities Enrollments
(Relative Frequency %)
Eliminate Responders not Offering Degree

Variable	N	Mean	Std Dev	Median	Q1	Q3
Male Und	27	17.50	19.27	10.42	7.69	22.73
Female Und	27	18.94	18.19	18.23	7.09	22.74
Total Und	29	18.31	17.58	16.40	9.07	21.54
Male Masters	29	10.50	19.06	4.76	0.00	12.50
Female Masters	29	14.98	26.26	9.24	3.36	12.09
Total Masters	31	10.72	17.29	8.07	3.17	11.35
Male Doctoral	23	22.46	38.80	0.00	0.00	33.33
Female Doctoral	29	14.72	18.23	10.84	7.53	14.29
Total Doctoral	31	14.01	17.85	10.34	5.88	14.29
Male Other	8	3.44	7.81	0.00	0.00	2.63
Female Other	11	7.58	7.17	7.69	0.00	14.96
Total Other	11	7.41	6.79	7.69	0.00	13.70
Male Total	30	14.40	18.14	9.84	6.98	14.29
Female Total	30	15.28	17.06	13.31	6.57	17.06
Total Enrolled	32	14.67	16.60	12.21	6.83	15.65

Table 1C(1) List of Mean and Median Responses to Part 1, Question C
Degrees Last Five Years

Variable	N	Mean	Std Dev	Median	Q1	Q3
Male Und	29	60.50	47.00	49.00	39.00	76.00
Female Und	29	532.40	383.20	491.00	352.00	740.00
Total Und	30	602.10	412.20	540.00	406.00	852.00
Male Masters	29	19.70	19.60	14.00	8.00	23.00
Female Masters	29	341.90	266.50	276.00	194.00	422.00
Total Masters	30	363.20	276.30	292.70	201.00	459.00
Male Doctoral	29	1.70	2.90	1.00	0.00	2.00
Female Doctoral	29	30.50	33.80	26.00	3.00	41.00
Total Doctoral	30	34.50	37.80	28.00	3.00	45.00
Male Other	29	0.20	0.70	0.00	0.00	0.00
Female Other	29	6.40	15.10	0.00	0.00	0.00
Total Other	30	6.40	15.20	0.00	0.00	0.00
Male Total	29	82.10	55.00	69.00	48.00	95.00
Female Total	29	911.20	416.90	917.00	696.00	1091.00
Total Degree	30	1006.10	450.20	1017.50	765.00	1201.00

Table 1C(2) List of Mean and Median Responses to Part 1, Question C
Degrees Last Five Years
Eliminate Responders Without Degree

Variable	N	Mean	Std Dev	Median	Q1	Q3
Male Und	26	67.40	44.50	55.80	41.00	78.00
Female Und	26	593.90	355.70	500.50	407.00	776.00
Total Und	27	669.00	378.30	557.00	448.00	869.00
Male Masters	27	21.10	19.50	15.00	9.00	23.00
Female Masters	27	367.20	258.50	290.00	210.00	445.00
Total Masters	28	389.10	267.50	311.70	225.00	466.50
Male Doctoral	23	2.20	3.10	1.00	0.00	2.00
Female Doctoral	23	38.50	33.70	31.00	13.00	45.00
Total Doctoral	24	43.10	37.70	33.00	16.00	52.00
Male Other	7	1.00	1.20	1.00	0.00	2.00
Female Other	7	26.40	21.00	19.00	12.00	40.00
Total Other	7	27.40	21.00	20.00	12.00	40.00
Male Total	29	82.10	55.00	69.00	48.00	95.00
Female Total	29	911.20	416.90	917.00	696.00	1091.00
Total Degree	30	1006.10	450.20	1017.50	765.00	1201.00

Table 1D(1) List of Mean and Median Responses to Part 1, Question D
Degrees in Last Five Years
Frequency Count for African American
Eliminate Responders Without Degree

Variable	N	Mean	Std Dev	Median	Q1	Q3
Male Und	27	2.11	2.76	2.00	0.00	3.00
Female Und	27	27.93	37.55	12.00	7.00	31.00
Total Und	29	34.45	44.69	15.00	9.00	34.00
Male Masters	27	0.56	1.09	0.00	0.00	1.00
Female Masters	27	11.93	13.90	7.00	1.00	24.00
Total Masters	29	13.38	14.74	9.00	2.00	25.00
Male Doctoral	28	0.04	0.19	0.00	0.00	0.00
Female Doctoral	28	1.46	2.46	0.50	0.00	1.50
Total Doctoral	29	1.45	2.43	0.00	0.00	2.00
Male Other	28	0.00	0.00	0.00	0.00	0.00
Female Other	28	0.18	0.77	0.00	0.00	0.00
Total Other	29	0.17	0.76	0.00	0.00	0.00
Male Total	27	2.70	3.05	2.00	1.00	3.00
Female Total	27	41.52	47.65	20.00	11.00	52.00
Total Degree	27	44.22	49.89	22.00	11.00	55.00

Table 1D(2) List of Mean and Median Responses to Part 1, Question D
Degrees in Last Five Years
Relative Frequency for African American
Eliminate Responders Without Degree

Variable	N	Mean	Std Dev	Median	Q1	Q3
Male Und	24	3.30	3.07	3.39	0.00	4.76
Female Und	24	7.22	11.19	3.58	2.02	6.49
Total Und	26	6.46	8.23	3.73	2.21	6.90
Male Masters	25	1.92	2.83	0.00	0.00	4.08
Female Masters	25	3.07	2.85	2.36	1.02	3.59
Total Masters	27	3.41	3.13	2.53	0.95	5.27
Male Doctoral	15	1.11	4.30	0.00	0.00	0.00
Female Doctoral	22	4.07	4.77	2.47	0.00	7.14
Total Doctoral	23	3.72	4.42	2.33	0.00	6.90
Male Other	4	0.00	0.00	0.00	0.00	0.00
Female Other	7	1.49	2.57	0.00	0.00	4.55
Total Other	7	1.42	2.48	0.00	0.00	4.17
Male Total	27	3.06	2.55	2.83	1.19	4.76
Female Total	27	4.24	4.07	3.00	1.95	5.25
Total Degree	27	4.13	3.78	3.11	2.11	4.93

Table 1D(3) List of Mean and Median Responses to Part 1, Question D
Degrees in Last Five Years
Frequency Count for Asian
Eliminate Responders Without Degree

Variable	N	Mean	Std Dev	Median	Q1	Q3
Male Und	27	2.19	2.35	1.00	0.00	4.00
Female Und	27	16.44	18.18	12.00	4.00	21.00
Total Und	29	20.14	20.29	15.00	6.00	27.00
Male Masters	27	0.59	1.12	0.00	0.00	1.00
Female Masters	27	12.38	20.96	4.00	1.00	11.00
Total Masters	29	12.32	21.13	4.00	2.00	11.00
Male Doctoral	28	0.00	0.00	0.00	0.00	0.00
Female Doctoral	28	0.85	1.66	0.00	0.00	1.00
Total Doctoral	29	0.89	1.65	0.00	0.00	1.00
Male Other	28	0.00	0.00	0.00	0.00	0.00
Female Other	28	0.07	0.38	0.00	0.00	0.00
Total Other	29	0.07	0.37	0.00	0.00	0.00
Male Total	27	2.78	2.38	3.00	1.00	5.00
Female Total	27	29.78	30.09	17.00	10.00	33.00
Total Degree	27	32.56	31.49	19.00	13.00	38.00

Table 1D(4) List of Mean and Median Responses to Part 1, Question D
Degrees in Last Five Years
Relative Frequency for Asian
Eliminate Responders Without Degree

Variable	N	Mean	Std Dev	Median	Q1	Q3
Male Und	24	3.92	3.91	3.32	0.00	5.51
Female Und	24	7.63	18.55	2.56	1.06	4.36
Total Und	26	5.74	10.24	2.74	1.20	5.03
Male Masters	25	2.88	6.51	0.00	0.00	3.45
Female Masters	25	2.64	3.13	1.64	1.06	3.75
Total Masters	27	2.53	3.07	1.54	1.02	3.52
Male Doctoral	15	0.00	0.00	0.00	0.00	0.00
Female Doctoral	22	2.96	4.46	0.43	0.00	3.70
Total Doctoral	23	2.90	4.03	0.81	0.00	5.37
Male Other	4	0.00	0.00	0.00	0.00	0.00
Female Other	7	0.42	1.11	0.00	0.00	0.00
Total Other	7	0.41	1.10	0.00	0.00	0.00
Male Total	27	3.59	3.39	3.16	0.87	4.92
Female Total	27	3.23	3.14	1.96	1.15	4.20
Total Degree	27	3.25	3.07	2.05	1.26	4.49

Table 1D(5) List of Mean and Median Responses to Part 1, Question D
Degrees in Last Five Years
Frequency Count for Hispanic
Eliminate Responders Without Degree

Variable	N	Mean	Std Dev	Median	Q1	Q3
Male Und	27	3.69	9.67	1.00	0.00	3.00
Female Und	27	18.35	40.84	6.00	3.00	22.00
Total Und	29	21.31	48.66	7.00	4.00	19.00
Male Masters	27	0.41	1.25	0.00	0.00	0.00
Female Masters	27	6.43	11.03	2.00	0.00	6.00
Total Masters	29	6.54	11.70	2.00	0.00	6.00
Male Doctoral	28	0.11	0.31	0.00	0.00	0.00
Female Doctoral	28	0.32	0.72	0.00	0.00	0.00
Total Doctoral	29	0.41	0.82	0.00	0.00	1.00
Male Other	28	0.00	0.00	0.00	0.00	0.00
Female Other	28	0.14	0.59	0.00	0.00	0.00
Total Other	29	0.14	0.58	0.00	0.00	0.00
Male Total	27	4.21	9.85	2.00	0.00	3.00
Female Total	27	25.15	44.83	12.00	4.00	31.00
Total Degree	27	29.36	54.52	13.00	5.00	34.00

Table 1D(6) List of Mean and Median Responses to Part 1, Question D
Degrees in Last Five Years
Relative Frequency for Hispanic
Eliminate Responders Without Degree

Variable	N	Mean	Std Dev	Median	Q1	Q3
Male Und	24	4.91	6.51	2.93	1.30	5.41
Female Und	24	4.13	5.96	1.53	0.78	4.88
Total Und	26	3.70	5.21	1.58	0.84	3.68
Male Masters	25	0.98	2.63	0.00	0.00	0.00
Female Masters	25	1.51	1.75	0.84	0.40	1.35
Total Masters	27	1.44	1.69	0.81	0.37	1.53
Male Doctoral	15	13.85	35.03	0.00	0.00	0.00
Female Doctoral	22	0.74	1.72	0.00	0.00	0.86
Total Doctoral	23	1.32	2.44	0.00	0.00	1.72
Male Other	4	0.00	0.00	0.00	0.00	0.00
Female Other	7	2.89	7.02	0.00	0.00	1.47
Total Other	7	2.46	5.90	0.00	0.00	1.45
Male Total	27	3.70	4.52	2.60	0.00	4.35
Female Total	27	2.62	3.80	1.22	0.53	3.41
Total Degree	27	2.70	3.81	1.28	0.56	3.28

Table 1D(7) List of Mean and Median Responses to Part 1, Question D
Degrees in Last Five Years
Frequency Count for Native American
Eliminate Responders Without Degree

Variable	N	Mean	Std Dev	Median	Q1	Q3
Male Und	27	0.21	0.46	0.00	0.00	0.00
Female Und	27	1.74	2.03	1.00	0.00	3.00
Total Und	29	1.99	2.16	1.00	0.00	3.00
Male Masters	27	0.11	0.32	0.00	0.00	0.00
Female Masters	27	1.33	1.86	1.00	0.00	2.00
Total Masters	29	1.34	1.86	1.00	0.00	1.00
Male Doctoral	28	0.00	0.00	0.00	0.00	0.00
Female Doctoral	28	0.18	0.55	0.00	0.00	0.00
Total Doctoral	29	0.17	0.54	0.00	0.00	0.00
Male Other	28	0.00	0.00	0.00	0.00	0.00
Female Other	28	0.04	0.19	0.00	0.00	0.00
Total Other	29	0.03	0.19	0.00	0.00	0.00
Male Total	27	0.32	0.52	0.00	0.00	1.00
Female Total	27	3.30	2.96	3.00	1.00	6.00
Total Degree	27	3.62	3.01	3.00	1.00	6.00

Table 1D(8) List of Mean and Median Responses to Part 1, Question D
Degrees in Last Five Years
Relative Frequency for Native American
Eliminate Responders Without Degree

Variable	N	Mean	Std Dev	Median	Q1	Q3
Male Und	24	0.28	0.70	0.00	0.00	0.00
Female Und	24	0.40	0.50	0.20	0.08	0.41
Total Und	26	0.38	0.45	0.21	0.15	0.36
Male Masters	25	0.60	2.27	0.00	0.00	0.00
Female Masters	25	0.35	0.40	0.28	0.00	0.52
Total Masters	27	0.34	0.37	0.27	0.00	0.53
Male Doctoral	15	0.00	0.00	0.00	0.00	0.00
Female Doctoral	22	0.50	1.59	0.00	0.00	0.00
Total Doctoral	23	0.45	1.50	0.00	0.00	0.00
Male Other	4	0.00	0.00	0.00	0.00	0.00
Female Other	7	0.21	0.56	0.00	0.00	0.00
Total Other	7	0.21	0.55	0.00	0.00	0.00
Male Total	27	0.32	0.60	0.00	0.00	0.61
Female Total	27	0.40	0.41	0.30	0.13	0.55
Total Degree	27	0.40	0.40	0.28	0.15	0.55

Table 1D(9) List of Mean and Median Responses to Part 1, Question D
Degrees in Last Five Years
Frequency Count for Total Minorities
Eliminate Responders Without Degree

Variable	N	Mean	Std Dev	Median	Q1	Q3
Male Und	27	8.20	13.16	5.00	2.00	9.00
Female Und	27	64.46	71.80	45.00	16.00	91.00
Total Und	28	77.99	86.39	54.00	20.50	104.30
Male Masters	27	1.67	3.10	0.00	0.00	2.00
Female Masters	27	32.07	41.86	18.00	4.00	38.00
Total Masters	29	33.59	42.83	22.00	8.00	41.00
Male Doctoral	28	0.14	0.36	0.00	0.00	0.00
Female Doctoral	28	2.81	4.20	1.33	0.00	4.00
Total Doctoral	29	2.92	4.28	2.00	0.00	4.00
Male Other	28	0.00	0.00	0.00	0.00	0.00
Female Other	28	0.43	1.60	0.00	0.00	0.00
Total Other	29	0.41	1.57	0.00	0.00	0.00
Male Total	27	10.01	13.27	7.00	3.00	13.00
Female Total	27	99.74	88.06	91.00	31.00	146.00
Total Degree	28	115.40	101.20	97.00	34.00	161.00

Table 1D(10) List of Mean and Median Responses to Part 1, Question D
Degrees in Last Five Years
Relative Frequency for Total Minorities
Eliminate Responders Without Degree

Variable	N	Mean	Std Dev	Median	Q1	Q3
Male Und	24	12.41	8.41	11.78	5.85	16.48
Female Und	24	19.38	30.32	11.66	5.35	16.57
Total Und	25	16.60	18.44	12.07	6.08	16.47
Male Masters	25	6.39	9.34	0.00	0.00	9.52
Female Masters	25	7.57	5.62	7.55	3.60	9.54
Total Masters	27	7.72	5.52	7.64	3.49	9.57
Male Doctoral	15	14.96	34.83	0.00	0.00	7.69
Female Doctoral	22	8.26	6.24	7.33	3.23	11.54
Total Doctoral	23	8.40	6.31	6.90	3.23	13.42
Male Other	4	0.00	0.00	0.00	0.00	0.00
Female Other	7	5.01	7.47	0.00	0.00	11.76
Total Other	7	4.51	6.57	0.00	0.00	11.59
Male Total	27	10.66	7.04	9.84	5.22	16.39
Female Total	27	10.49	7.48	10.33	4.32	14.11
Total Degree	28	10.86	7.33	10.21	4.48	14.75

Part II: Recruitment

Table II: List of responses by category	
Category/Response	**Frequency**
Coordinate with campus wide programs for minority recruiting:	
Participate in campus wide minority recruiting activities (unspecified)	13
Special open house programs/career days for minorities on campus	8
Work through/organize minority student groups on campus	4
Participate in summer research program for minorities	3
Appear at minority recruitment fairs on campus	3
Use Minority Affairs recruiter	1
Work with Medical Center Minority recruiter	1
Participate in summer camps for minorities	1
Resources:	
Scholarships/grants in aid targeted to minorities	8
Advertise in publications targeted to minorities	6
Hire part time recruiter	1
Created staff position for minority recruiting/retention	1
Send faculty on recruiting trips	1
Pay expenses for minority students to visit campus	1
Sponsor a Black and Hispanic Nurse Symposia	1
Career Fairs:	
Attend Career Days/Health Fairs targeted to minorities	7
Minority Recruitment Fair	1
Minority College Career Day	1
Work with feeder institutions:	
Work with feeder schools (sometimes these are Community Colleges)	5
Emphasize feeder schools having predominantly minority populations	5
Visit High Schools	5
Work with High School counselors	3
Target colleges/universities having underrepresented groups	3
Associate with or contact HBCUs	2
Mentor minorities at High School level	2
Work with Community College advisors	1
Adopt a School Program	1
Recruit out of state	1
Work with minority professional organizations	1
Targeted Contacts:	
Personal contacts	7
Minority faculty help recruit	2
Shadowing program	2
Special mailing to prospective minority students	1
Other Strategies:	
Form a Faculty Recruitment and Retention Committee	1
Have senior minority students mentor junior minority students	1
Get alumni to help	1

Rating of Panel Members and Students on Criteria

Recruitment

A. The University/College/School of Nursing interested in recruiting minorities (African-Americans, Asians, Latinos (Hispanics), and/or Native Americans) should:

Ranked		
Fellows	*Experts*	
1	1	1. See that the recruitment of nursing students is part of the University's effort and involves the administrator responsible for students, admissions, registration and other pertinent entities on the campus.
3	2	2. Develop packages which provide information on admission criteria, standardized test scores, requirements for graduation, financial aid, housing, student health, student fees (e.g., for computers, activities, and laboratories), support services (e.g., counseling, child care, writing and speaking laboratories, and tutorial assistance).
5	3	3. Market nursing better and assure that the information about nursing is provided to inform the public and particularly to assist high school counselors.
2	5	4. Assure that the nature of nursing and its options for career development are better presented.
4	4	5. Orient recruiters so that they not only have an understanding of the nursing program but an understanding of the expectations of the University (e.g. general education requirements, assessing support services, etc.)
6	6	6. Be aware of different learning styles of students and have ways of assessing how best to help students admitted to the program be successful.

B. The recruiter of minority students for programs in nursing should:

Ranked		
Fellows	*Experts*	
2	5	1. Represent the same minority background as the individual(s) being recruited or have some connection with the community from which the student is being recruited.

___4___   ___2___   2. Collaborate with the community of the targeted population from which the individual(s) are being recruited to secure resolution from and endorsement of the community.

___1___   ___1___   3. Be aware of family influence on the prospective recruit(s) and recognize the nature of the impact on the family of the recruit being enrolled in a nursing program in an institutional setting.

___3___   ___4___   4. Elicit the help of an advisory group composed of representatives of a targeted population from which the individual(s) are being recruited.

___5___   ___3___   5. Recognize the perception of family and recruit about the profession of nursing and be prepared to discuss the length of the program, the types of programs, the varied opportunities nursing presents and the potential growth in the discipline.

Retention

A. The institution has a positive valuation of multiculturalism and this is demonstrated in the following ways:

Ranked
Fellows   Experts

___2___   ___3___   1. Provides administrative support of cultural diversity in the faculty and students.

___1___   ___1___   2. Allocates resources to further the initiatives that assure support of cultural diversity.

___3___   ___5___   3. Requires a systematic and periodic evaluation of programs offered by the University and an aspect of that evaluation considers diversity of faculty and students.

___5___   ___2___   4. Recognizes the importance of cultural enrichment in programs and considers the moral, political, economic and global dimensions.

___4___   ___4___   5. Builds multiple strategies and means to facilitate minority faculty and student success.

B. The nursing program administration:

Ranked
Fellows   Experts

___3___   ___1___   1. Creates an environment of open communication.

5	5	2. Commits to leadership development of minority students along with other students enrolled in the program.
8	6	3. Utilizes variance in measuring achievement and is sensitive to cultural variance.
1	7	4. Has clear expectations of students and delineates them to students who are admitted to the program.
2	2	5. Provides the administrative support that will enable a student to succeed.
6	8	6. Provides both internal and external mentors for students.
7	3	7. Helps faculty and staff recognize and acknowledge the value and influence of family for many minority groups.
9	9	8. Balance flexible accommodation of special circumstances with cultivation of professional norms and standards.
4	4	9. Capitalize on and provide existing technological tools (e.g., distance learning, learning modules, computer aided instruction) to maximize alternative learning opportunities.

C. The faculty of the nursing program:

Ranked
Fellows *Experts*

8	8	1. Admits only those students the faculty believes will be able to succeed.
1	4	2. Provides means to help students understand the curriculum and what is expected through effective communication, collaboration and group skills.
4	5	3. Provides counseling and advising for anticipated student needs.
7	3	4. Helps students with negotiating skills and how to access available resources.
6	6	5. Helps students learn effective use of assertiveness skills.
3	1	6. Coordinates mentoring and assures that the process of linking students with people who can assist them is effective.
5	7	7. Helps students learn to resolve conflict.
2	2	8. Provide students with skills to adopt to the institutional culture without losing their own identity.

GRADUATION

A. The following are essential environmental elements that exist in the institution for students to successfully matriculate and graduate:

Ranked

Fellows   Experts

Fellows	Experts	
2	2	1. There must be resocialization of the faculty to create a successful oriented milieu.
3	3	2. There must be interaction and communication between majority and minority students and faculty.
4	1	3. Every effort must be made to eliminate cognitive dissonance between majority and minority individuals and the creation of psychological and physical comfort between the individuals.
1	4	4. Every effort must be made to select deans, chairs and faculty who have the capacity to respect and empower others and who possess self-esteem and value the contributions of others.

B. An institution which facilitates and promotes graduation has the following implements on behalf of its students:

Ranked

Fellows   Experts

Fellows	Experts	
5	4	1. It enhances student socialization in that it values people.
1	1	2. It connects the student with resources (financial, library, computers, writing assistance, speaking assistance, advisors, models of successful people, participation in work with successful faculty, study groups and tutors).
4	2	3. It provides intellectual stimulation for students.
2	5	4. It sets forth indicators of the acquisition of knowledge for students.
3	3	5. It provides supplemental opportunities for the enhancement of student learning if warranted (e.g., additional clinical activity).

C. An institution that is committed to students being productive has these environmental elements:

Ranked

Fellows   Experts

Fellows	Experts	
2	1	1. It clearly identifies the value of people as intellectual, economic, social and moral capital.

5	4	2. It recognizes that the failure to promote and graduate students results in serious casualties such as individuals who are dysfunctional, frozen in careers, or who are subject to rage and consequently immobilization of talent.
4	2	3. It creates a desire for and emphasizes principles of justice, ethics, and intellectual honesty.
3	3	4. It transmits the joy of learning and a thirst for new knowledge.
1	5	5. It establishes a contractual relationship between the student and the faculty member in which the roles of student and faculty are clearly delineated and understood.

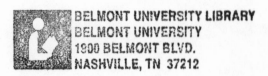
DATE DUE

OCT 0 8 2001			
OCT 2 2 2001			
OCT 2 2 REC'D			
NOV 1 4 2001			
DEC 0 2 REC'D			
OCT 1 4 2002			
NOV 2 2 REC'D			
GAYLORD			PRINTED IN U.S.A.